CHRISTIAN TEMPERANCE

AND

BIBLE HYGIENE

CHRISTIAN TEMPERANCE

By MRS. E. G. WHITE

AND

BIBLE HYGIENE

By ELD. JAMES WHITE

TEACH Services, Inc.
New York

2005 06 07 08 09 10 11 12 · 5 4 3 2 1

Copyright © 2005 TEACH Services, Inc.
ISBN-13: 978-1-57258-306-1
ISBN-10: 1-57258-306-1
Library of Congress Catalog Card No. 2005921415

Published by
TEACH Services, Inc.
www.TEACHServices.com

PREFACE.

NEARLY thirty years ago there appeared in print the first of a series of remarkable and important articles on the subject of health, by Mrs. E. G. White. These articles at once commanded earnest consideration by those who were acquainted with Mrs. White's previous writings and labors. Thousands were led to change life-long habits, and to renounce practices thoroughly fixed by heredity as well as by long indulgence. So great a revolution could not be wrought in a body of people without the aid of some powerful incentive, which in this case was undoubtedly the belief that the writings referred to not only bore the stamp of truth, but were indorsed as such by a higher than human authority. This is not the proper place for the consideration of the grounds upon which this belief was based, but the reader's attention is invited to a few facts of interest in this connection : —

1. At the time the writings referred to first appeared, the subject of health was almost wholly ignored, not only by the people to whom they were addressed, but by the world at large.

2. The few advocating the necessity of a reform in physical habits, propagated in connection with the advocacy of genuine reformatory principles the most patent and in some instances disgusting errors.

3. Nowhere, and by no one, was there presented a systematic and harmonious body of hygienic truths, free from patent errors, and consistent with the Bible and the principles of the Christian religion.

Under these circumstances, the writings referred to made their appearance. The principles taught were not enforced by scientific authority, but were presented in a simple, straightforward manner by one who makes no pretense to scientific knowledge, but claims to write by the aid and authority of the divine enlightenment.

How have the principles presented under such peculiar circumstances and with such remarkable claims stood the test of time and experience ? is a question which may very properly be asked. Its answer is to be found in facts which are capable of the amplest verification. The principles presented have been put to the test of practical experience by thousands ; and whenever intelligently and consistently carried out, the result has been found in the highest degree satisfactory. Thousands have testified to physical, mental, and moral benefits received. Many of the principles taught have come to be so generally adopted and practiced that they are no longer recognized as reforms, and may, in fact, be regarded as prevalent customs among the more intelligent classes. The principles which a quarter of a century ago were either entirely ignored or made the butt of ridicule, have quietly won their way into public confidence and esteem, until the world has quite forgotten that they have not always been thus accepted. New discoveries in science and new interpretations of old facts have continually added confirmatory evidence, until at the present time every one of the principles advocated more than a quarter of a century ago is fortified in the strongest possible manner by scientific evidence.

Finally, the reformatory movement based upon the principles advocated so long ago has lived and prospered until the present time, and the institutions developed by it have grown to be the most extensive and the most prosperous establishments of the sort in the world; while other efforts, looking somewhat in the same direction, but contaminated by error, have either abandoned the principles of truth, and been given over to error, or have fallen into obscurity. It certainly must be regarded as a thing remarkable, and evincing unmistakable evidence of divine insight and direction, that in the midst of confused and conflicting teachings, claiming the authority of science and experience, but warped by ultra notions and rendered impotent for good by the great admixture of error,— it must be admitted to be something extraordinary, that a person making no claims to scientific knowledge or erudition should have been able to organize, from the confused and error-tainted mass of ideas advanced by a few writers and thinkers on health subjects, a body of hygienic principles so harmonious, so consistent, and so genuine that the discussions, the researches, the discoveries, and the experience of a quarter of a century have not resulted in the overthrow of a single principle, but have only served to establish the doctrines taught.

The guidance of infinite wisdom is as much needed in discerning between truth and error as in the evolution of new truths. Novelty is by no means a distinguishing characteristic of true principles, and the principle holds good as regards the truths of hygienic reform, as well as those of other reformatory movements. The greatest and most important reformatory movements of modern times have not been those which presented new facts and principles, but those which revived truths and principles long forgotten, and which have led the way back to the paths trodden by men of by-gone ages, before the world had wandered so far away from physical and moral rectitude.

This book is not a new presentation of the principles referred to in the above paragraphs, but is simply a compilation, and in some sense an abstract, of the various writings of Mrs. White upon this subject, to which have been added several articles, by Elder James White, elucidating the same principles, and the personal experience of Elders J. N. Andrews and Joseph Bates, two of the pioneers in the health movement among Seventh-day Adventists. The work of compilation has been done under the supervision of Mrs. White, by a committee appointed by her for the purpose, and the manuscript has been carefully examined by her.

The purpose in the preparation of this volume has been to gather together, in a condensed form, writings which were scattered through various volumes, and some that have never before appeared in print, so that the teachings of Mrs. White upon this subject might reach as large a number as possible of those for whom they were specially intended; and it is confidently believed that the work will receive a cordial reception, and the earnest consideration which its importance demands.

CONTENTS.

CHRISTIAN TEMPERANCE.

BIBLE HYGIENE.

vi   CONTENTS.

CHRISTIAN TEMPERANCE.

GENERAL PRINCIPLES.

MAN came from the hand of his Creator perfect in organization and beautiful in form. The fact that he has for six thousand years withstood the ever-increasing weight of disease and crime is conclusive proof of the power of endurance with which he was first endowed. And although the antediluvians generally gave themselves up to sin without restraint, it was more than two thousand years before the violation of natural law was sensibly felt. Had Adam originally possessed no greater physical power than men now have, the race would ere this have become extinct.

Through the successive generations since the fall, the tendency has been continually downward. Disease has been transmitted from parents to children, generation after generation. Even infants in the cradle suffer from afflictions caused by the sins of their parents.

Moses, the first historian, gives quite a definite account of social and individual life in the early days of the world's history, but we find no record that an infant was born blind, deaf, crippled, or imbecile. Not an instance is recorded of a natural death in infancy, childhood, or early manhood. Obituary notices in the book of Genesis run thus: "And all the days that Adam lived were nine hundred and thirty years; and he died." "And all the days of Seth were nine hundred and twelve years; and he died." Concerning others the record states, "He died in a good old age, an old man, and full of years." It was so rare for a son to die before his father, that such an occurrence was considered worthy of record: "Haran died before his father Terah."* The patriarchs from Adam to Noah, with few exceptions, lived nearly a thousand years. Since then the average length of life has been decreasing.

At the time of Christ's first advent, the race had already so degenerated that not only the old, but the middle-aged and the young, were brought from every city to the Saviour, to be healed of their diseases. Many labored under a weight of misery inexpressible.

The violation of physical law, with its consequent suffering and premature death, has so long prevailed that these results are regarded as the appointed lot of humanity; but God did not create the race in such a feeble condition. This state of things is not the work of Providence, but of man. It has been brought about by wrong habits, — by violating the laws that God has made to govern man's existence. A continual transgression of nature's laws is a continual transgression of the law of God. Had men always been obedient to the law of the ten commandments, carrying out in their lives the principles of those precepts, the curse of disease now flooding the world would not exist.

"Know ye not that your body is the temple of the Holy Ghost which is in you, which ye have of God, and ye are not your own? for ye are bought with a price; therefore glorify God in your body and in your spirit, which are God's."† When men take any course which needlessly expends their vitality or beclouds their intellect, they sin against God; they do not glorify him in their body and spirit, which are his.

Yet despite the insult which man has offered him, God's love is still extended to the race; and he permits light to shine, enabling man to see that in order to live a perfect life he must obey the natural laws which govern his being. How important, then, that man should walk in this light, exercising all his powers, both of body and mind, to the glory of God!

We are in a world that is opposed to righteousness, or purity of character, and especially to growth in grace. Wherever we look, we see defilement and corruption, de-

---

Gen. 5: 5, 8: 25: 8; 11: 28.   † 1 Cor. 6: 19.

formity and sin. How opposed is all this to the work that must be accomplished in us just previous to receiving the gift of immortality! God's elect must stand untainted amid the corruptions teeming around them in these last days. Their bodies must be made holy, their spirits pure. If this work is to be accomplished, it must be undertaken at once, earnestly and understandingly. The Spirit of God should have perfect control, influencing every action.

The health reform is one branch of the great work which is to fit a people for the coming of the Lord. It is as closely connected with the third angel's message as the hand is with the body. The law of ten commandments has been lightly regarded by man; yet the Lord will not come to punish the transgressors of that law without first sending them a message of warning. Men and women cannot violate natural law by indulging depraved appetite and lustful passions, without violating the law of God. Therefore he has permitted the light of health reform to shine upon us, that we may realize the sinfulness of breaking the laws which he has established in our very being. Our heavenly Father sees the deplorable condition of men who, many of them ignorantly, are disregarding the principles of hygiene. And it is in love and pity to the race that he causes the light to shine upon health reform. He publishes his law and its penalties, in order that all may learn what is for their highest good. He proclaims his law so distinctly, and makes it so prominent, that it is like a city set on a hill. All intelligent beings can understand it if they will. None others are responsible. To make natural law plain, and to urge obedience to it, is a work that accompanies the third angel's message.

Ignorance is no excuse now for the transgression of law. The light shines clearly, and none need be ignorant; for the great God himself is man's instructor. All are bound by the most sacred obligations to heed the sound philosophy and genuine experience which God is now giving them in reference to health reform. He designs that the subject shall be agitated, and the public mind deeply stirred to investigate it; for it is impossible for men and women, while under the power of sinful, health-destroying, brain-enervating habits, to appreciate sacred truth. Those who are willing to inform themselves concerning the effect which sinful indulgence has upon the health, and who begin the work of reform, even from selfish motives, may in so doing place themselves where the truth of God can reach their hearts. And, on the other hand, those who have been reached by the presentation of Scripture truth are in a position where the conscience may be aroused upon the subject of health. They see and feel the necessity of breaking away from the tyrannizing habits and appetites which have ruled them so long. There are many who would receive the truths of God's word, their judgment having been convinced by the clearest evidence; but the carnal desires, clamoring for gratification, control the intellect, and they reject truth because it conflicts with their lustful desires. The minds of many take so low a level that God cannot work either for them or with them. The current of their thoughts must be changed, their moral sensibilities must be aroused, before they can feel the claims of God.

The apostle Paul exhorts the church, " I beseech you therefore, brethren, by the mercies of God, that ye present your bodies a living sacrifice, holy, acceptable unto God, which is your reasonable service." * Sinful indulgence defiles the body, and unfits men for spiritual worship. He who cherishes the light which God has given him upon health reform, has an important aid in the work of becoming sanctified through the truth, and fitted for immortality. But if he disregards that light, and lives in violation of natural law, he must pay the penalty; his spiritual powers are benumbed, and how can he perfect holiness in the fear of God?

Men have polluted the soul-temple, and God calls upon them to awake, and to strive with all their might to win

* Rom. 12 : 1.

back their God-given manhood. Nothing but the grace
of God can convict and convert the heart; from him
alone can the slaves of custom obtain power to break
the shackles that bind them. It is impossible for a man
to present his body a living sacrifice, holy, acceptable to
God, while continuing to indulge habits that are depriving him of physical, mental, and moral vigor. Again the
apostle says, "Be not conformed to this world; but be
ye transformed by the renewing of your mind, that ye
may prove what is that good, and acceptable, and perfect
will of God." *

Jesus, seated on the Mount of Olives, gave instruction
to his disciples concerning the signs which should pre-
cede his coming: "As the days of Noah were, so shall
also the coming of the Son of man be. For as in the
days that were before the flood they were eating and
drinking, marrying and giving in marriage, until the day
that Noah entered into the ark, and knew not until the
flood came and took them all away; so shall also the
coming of the Son of man be." † The same sins that
brought judgments upon the world in the days of Noah,
exist in our day. Men and women now carry their eating and drinking so far that it ends in gluttony and
drunkenness. This prevailing sin, the indulgence of perverted appetite, inflamed the passions of men in the days
of Noah, and led to wide-spread corruption. Violence
and sin reached to heaven. This moral pollution was
finally swept from the earth by means of the flood. The
same sins of gluttony and drunkenness benumbed the
moral sensibilities of the inhabitants of Sodom, so that
crime seemed to be the delight of the men and women
of that wicked city. Christ thus warns the world: "Likewise also as it was in the days of Lot; they did eat,
they drank, they bought, they sold, they planted, they
builded; but the same day that Lot went out of Sodom
it rained fire and brimstone from heaven, and destroyed
them all. Even thus shall it be in the day when the
Son of man is revealed." ‡

* Rom. 12 : 2.   † Matt. 24 : 37-39.   ‡ Luke 17 : 28-30.

Christ has here left us a most important lesson. He would lay before us the danger of making our eating and drinking paramount. He presents the result of unrestrained indulgence of appetite. The moral powers are enfeebled, so that sin does not appear sinful. Crime is lightly regarded, and passion controls the mind, until good principles and impulses are rooted out, and God is blasphemed. All this is the result of eating and drinking to excess. This is the very condition of things which Christ declares will exist at his second coming.

The Saviour presents to us something higher to toil for than merely what we shall eat and drink, and wherewithal we shall be clothed. Eating, drinking, and dressing are carried to such excess that they become crimes. They are among the marked sins of the last days, and constitute a sign of Christ's soon coming. Time, money, and strength, which belong to the Lord, but which he has intrusted to us, are wasted in superfluities of dress and luxuries for the perverted appetite, which lessen vitality, and bring suffering and decay. It is impossible to present our bodies a living sacrifice to God when we continually fill them with corruption and disease by our own sinful indulgence.

Knowledge must be gained in regard to how to eat and drink and dress so as to preserve health. Sickness is the result of violating nature's law. Our first duty, one which we owe to God, to ourselves, and to our fellowmen, is to obey the laws of God. These include the laws of health. If we are sick, we impose a weary tax upon our friends, and unfit ourselves for doing our duty either in the family or to our neighbors. And when premature death is the result, we bring sorrow and suffering to others; we deprive our neighbors of the help we might have rendered them; we rob our families of the comfort and help which they should have received from us, and rob God of the service he claims of us to advance his glory. Then are we not, in a high sense, transgressors of God's law?

But God is compassionate and tender, and when light comes to those who have injured themselves by sinful indulgence, if they repent and seek pardon, he mercifully accepts them. But what an inferior, pitiful offering at best, to present to a pure and holy God! O, what tender mercy, that he does not refuse the poor remnant of the life of the suffering, repenting sinner! Praise be to God, who saves such souls as by fire!

The view held by some that spirituality is a detriment to health, is the sophistry of Satan. The religion of the Bible is not detrimental to the health of either body or mind. The influence of the Spirit of God is the very best medicine for disease. Heaven is all health; and the more deeply heavenly influences are realized, the more sure will be the recovery of the believing invalid. The true principles of Christianity open before all a source of inestimable happiness. Religion is a continual well-spring, from which the Christian can drink at will, and never exhaust the fountain.

The relation which exists between the mind and the body is very intimate. When one is affected, the other sympathizes. The condition of the mind affects the health of the physical system. If the mind is free and happy, from a consciousness of right-doing and a sense of satisfaction in causing happiness to others, it creates a cheerfulness that will react upon the whole system, causing a freer circulation of the blood, and a toning up of the entire body. The blessing of God is a healing power, and those who are abundant in benefiting others will realize that wondrous blessing in both heart and life.

When men who have indulged in wrong habits and sinful practices yield to the power of divine truth, the application of that truth to the heart revives the moral powers, which had seemed to be paralyzed. The receiver possesses stronger, clearer understanding than before he riveted his soul to the eternal Rock. Even his physical health improves by the realization of his security in Christ. The special blessing of God resting upon the receiver is of itself health and strength.

Those who walk in the path of wisdom and holiness, find that "godliness is profitable unto all things, having promise of the life that now is, and of that which is to come."* They are alive to the enjoyment of life's real pleasures, and are not troubled with vain regrets over misspent hours, nor with gloomy forebodings, as the worldling too often is when not diverted by some exciting amusement. Godliness does not conflict with the laws of health, but is in harmony with them. The fear of the Lord is the foundation of all real prosperity.

* 1 Tim. 4 : 8.

OUR REASONABLE SERVICE.

"I BESEECH you therefore, brethren, by the mercies of God, that ye present your bodies a living sacrifice, holy, acceptable unto God, which is your reasonable service. And be not conformed to this world, but be ye transformed by the renewing of your mind, that ye may prove what is that good, and acceptable, and perfect will of God."*

In the ancient Jewish service it was required that every sacrifice should be without blemish. In the text we are told to present our bodies a living sacrifice, holy, acceptable unto God, which is our reasonable service. We are God's workmanship. The psalmist, meditating upon the marvelous work of God in the human frame, exclaimed, "I am fearfully and wonderfully made."† There are many who are educated in the sciences, and are familiar with the theory of the truth, who do not understand the laws that govern their own being. God has given us faculties and talents; and it is our duty, as his sons and daughters, to make the best use of them. If we weaken these powers of mind or body by wrong habits or indulgence of perverted appetite, it will be impossible for us to honor God as we should.

We can understand the value of the human soul only as we realize the greatness of the sacrifice made for its redemption. The word of God declares that we are not our own, that we are bought with a price. It is at an immense cost that we have been placed upon vantage ground, where we can find liberty from the bondage of sin wrought by the fall in Eden. Adam's sin plunged the race into hopeless misery; but by the sacrifice of the Son of God, a second probation was granted to man. In the plan of redemption a way of escape is provided for all who will avail themselves of it. God knew that it was impossible for man to overcome in his own strength, and

*Rom. 12 : 1, 2.   † Ps. 139 : 14.   (15)

he has provided help for him. How thankful we should be that a way is open for us, by which we can have access to the Father; that the gates are left ajar, so that beams of light from the glory within may shine upon those who will receive them!

Christ began the work of redemption just where the ruin began. His first test was on the same point where Adam failed. It was through temptations addressed to the appetite that Satan had overcome a large proportion of the human race, and his success had made him feel that the control of this fallen planet was in his hands. But in Christ he found one who was able to resist him, and he left the field of battle a conquered foe. Jesus says, He "hath nothing in me." * His victory is an assurance that we too may come off victors in our conflicts with the enemy. But it is not our heavenly Father's purpose to save us without an effort on our part to co-operate with Christ. We must act our part, and divine power, uniting with our effort, will bring victory.

We meet intemperance everywhere. We see it on the cars, the steamboats, and wherever we go; and we should ask ourselves what we are doing to rescue souls from the tempter's grasp. Satan is constantly on the alert to bring the race fully under his control. His strongest hold on man is through the appetite, and this he seeks to stimulate in every possible way. All unnatural excitants are harmful, and they cultivate the desire for liquor. How can we enlighten the people, and prevent the terrible evils that result from the use of these things? Have we done all that we can do in this direction?

Some will say that it is impossible to reclaim the drunkard, that efforts in this direction have failed again and again. But although we cannot reclaim all who have gone so far, we may do something to check the growth of the evil. I appeal to you, parents, to begin with your children, and give them a right education. Seek to bring them up so that they shall have moral stamina to resist the evil that surrounds them. The lesson of self-control

* John 14 : 30.

must begin with the child in its mother's arms. It must learn to restrain passionate temper, to bring its will into subjection, and to deny unhealthful cravings.

Teach your children to abhor stimulants. How many are ignorantly fostering in them an appetite for these things! In Europe I have seen nurses putting the glass of wine or beer to the lips of the innocent little ones, thus cultivating in them a taste for stimulants. As they grow older, they learn to depend more and more on these things, till little by little they are overcome, drift beyond the reach of help, and at last fill a drunkard's grave.

But it is not thus alone that the appetite is perverted and made a snare. The food is often such as to excite a desire for stimulating drinks. Luxurious dishes are placed before the children,— spiced foods, rich gravies, cakes, and pastries. This highly seasoned food irritates the stomach, and causes a craving for still stronger stimulants. Not only is the appetite tempted with unsuitable food, of which the children are allowed to eat freely at their meals, but they are permitted to eat between meals, and by the time they are twelve or fourteen years of age they are often confirmed dyspeptics.

You have perhaps seen a picture of the stomach of one who is addicted to strong drink. A similar condition is produced under the irritating influence of fiery spices. With the stomach in such a state, there is a craving for something more to meet the demands of the appetite, something stronger, and still stronger. Next you find your sons out on the street learning to smoke. It is a grievous lesson; it makes them deathly sick. Yet they press the matter through with a perseverance that would be praiseworthy in a better cause. Tobacco weakens the brain, and paralyzes its fine sensibilities. Its use excites a thirst for strong drink, and in very many cases lays the foundation for the liquor habit.

The use of tobacco is an inconvenient, expensive, uncleanly habit. The teachings of Christ, pointing to purity, self-denial, and temperance, all rebuke this defiling practice. When we think of the long fast that Jesus endured in the wilderness of temptation in order to break the power of appetite over man, we marvel that those who profess to be his followers can indulge in this habit. Is it for the glory of God for men to enfeeble the physical powers, confuse the brain, and yield the will to this narcotic poison? What right have they to mar the image of God? What says the apostle?—"I beseech you therefore, brethren, by the mercies of God, that ye present your bodies a living sacrifice, holy, acceptable unto God, which is your reasonable service."

A great responsibility rests upon us. We cannot render to God true service unless we present our bodies a living sacrifice. No one can be justified in marring this wonderfully intricate human organism. If we do this, not only do we suffer ourselves, but the evil is transmitted to our children. Can we wonder that the children who have such a legacy do not fear God? How often do we see boys not more than eight years old using tobacco! If you speak to them about it, they say, "My father uses it, and if it does him good, it will me." They point to the minister or the Sunday-school superintendent, and say, "If such good men as they use it, surely I can." How can we expect anything else of the children, with their inherited tendencies, while the older ones set them such an example? God pity the poor slave to these indulgences!

Both tobacco and liquor break down nerve force, and dull the finer perceptions, so that the slaves to these habits cannot discern between sacred and common things. An example of the demoralizing effect of intoxicants is seen in the case of Nadab and Abihu. They ventured to partake of wine before they entered the tabernacle to perform the duties of their sacred office, and the result was, they could not distinguish between common fire and that which was consecrated to the holy service. For this breach of trust they were slain. Some will say, "If they were intoxicated, and could not discern the difference between these fires, why should they be punished?" When they placed the cup to their lips, they made themselves responsible for all their deeds committed while under its influence.

How is it with our law makers, and the men in our courts of justice? If it was necessary that those who ministered in holy office should have clear minds and full control of their reason, is it not also important that those who make and execute the laws of our great nation should have their faculties unclouded? What about the judges and jurors, in whose hands rests the disposing of human life, and whose decisions may condemn the innocent, or turn the criminal loose upon society? Do they not need to have full control of their mental powers? Are they temperate in their habits? If not, they are not fit for such responsible positions. When the appetites are perverted, the mental powers are weakened, and there is danger that men will not rule justly. Is indulgence in that which beclouds the mind less dangerous to-day than when God placed restrictions upon those who ministered in holy office?

Christ fought the battle upon the point of appetite, and came off victorious; and we also can conquer through strength derived from him. Who will enter in through the gates into the city? — Not those who declare that they cannot break the force of appetite. Christ has resisted the power of him who would hold us in bondage; though weakened by his long fast of forty days, he withstood temptation, and proved by this act that our cases are not hopeless. I know that we cannot obtain the victory alone; and how thankful we should be that we have a living Saviour, who is ready and willing to aid us!

I recall the case of a man in a congregation that I was once addressing. He was almost wrecked in body and mind by the use of liquor and tobacco. He was bowed down from the effects of dissipation; and his dress was in keeping with his shattered condition. To all appearance he had gone too far to be reclaimed. But as I appealed to him to resist temptation in the strength of a risen Saviour, he rose tremblingly, and said, "You have an interest for me, and I will have an interest for myself." Six months afterward he came to my house. I did not recognize him. With a countenance beaming with joy, and eyes overflowing with tears, he grasped my hand, and said, "You do not know me, but you remember the man in an old blue coat who rose in your congregation, and said that he would try to reform?" I was astonished. He stood erect, and looked ten years younger. He had gone home from that meeting, and passed the long hours in prayer and struggle till the sun arose. It was a night of conflict, but, thank God, he came off a victor. This man could tell by sad experience of the bondage of these evil habits. He knew how to warn the youth of the dangers of contamination ; and those who, like himself, had been overcome, he could point to Christ as the only source of help.

In my travels I have witnessed scenes of feasting and revelry ; and as I have marked the effects of unrestrained indulgence, as I have listened to the blasphemous mirth, and seen the indifference and even contempt for all things sacred, I have thought of the sacrilegious feast of Belshazzar, to which were invited a thousand of his lords, his princes, his wives, and his concubines,— that feast where wine was freely drunk from the sacred vessels of the temple of God, while the revelers sang the praises of their gods of silver and gold. They knew not that an unseen Watcher heard every word of blasphemy, beheld every impious action.

In the midst of the revelry, Belshazzar saw the bloodless hand of an uninvited guest tracing upon the wall of the palace words that gleamed like fire,— words which, though unknown to that vast throng, were a portent of doom to the now conscience-stricken revelers. The boisterous mirth was hushed, and they shook with a nameless terror as their eyes fastened upon the wall. Where but a few moments before had been hilarity and blasphemous witticism, were pallid faces and cries of fear. A wild cry from the frantic king rang out in the assembly, calling for some one to come and read the writing. The wise men were called in, but those mystic characters were as strange to them as to the others.

Then the queen-mother remembered Daniel, who, so many years before, had made known to king Nebuchadnezzar his forgotten dream and its interpretation. Standing before that gorgeous, terror-stricken throng, the prophet of God reminded the king of Nebuchadnezzar's sin and fall, and reproved him for his own crimes. Then turning to the writing on the wall, he read the message from Heaven. The hand was gone, but four terrible words were left. With bated breath the people waited as Daniel announced their meaning: "*Mene, Mene, Tekel, Upharsin:*" "God hath numbered thy kingdom, and finished it;" "thou art weighed in the balances, and art found wanting;" "thy kingdom is divided, and given to the Medes and Persians." *

Just as surely as there was a Witness at the feast of Belshazzar, there is also a Witness in every scene of sacrilegious mirth, and just as surely is the recording angel writing, "Thou art weighed in the balances, and art found wanting."

Intemperance is on the increase, in spite of the efforts made to control it. We cannot be too earnest in seeking to hinder its progress, to raise the fallen, and shield the weak from temptation. With our feeble human hands we can do but little, but we have an unfailing Helper. We must not forget that the arm of Christ can reach to the very depths of human woe and degradation. He can give us help to conquer even this terrible demon of intemperance.

But it is in the home that the real work must begin. The greatest burden rests upon those who have the responsibility of educating the youth, of forming their character. Here is a work for mothers, in helping their children to form correct habits and pure tastes, to develop

* Dan. 5 : 25–28.

moral stamina, true moral worth. Teach them that they are not to be swayed by others, that they are not to yield to wrong influences, but to influence others for good, to ennoble and elevate those with whom they associate. Teach them that if they connect themselves with God, they will have strength from him to resist the fiercest temptations.

In the Babylonian court, Daniel was surrounded by allurements to sin, but by the help of Christ he maintained his integrity. He who cannot resist temptation, with every facility which has been placed within his reach, is not registered in the books of heaven as a man. The Lord never places men in positions so trying that it is beyond their power to withstand evil. Divine power is ever ready to protect and strengthen him who has been made a partaker of the divine nature.

Temptations to the indulgence of appetite possess a power which can be overcome only by the help that God can impart. But with every temptation we have the promise of God that there shall be a way of escape. Why, then, are so many overcome? It is because they do not put their trust in God. They do not avail themselves of the means provided for their safety. The excuses offered for the gratification of perverted appetite, are therefore of no weight with God.

Daniel valued his human capabilities, but he did not trust in them. His trust was in that strength which God has promised to all who will come to him in humble dependence, relying wholly upon his power.

He purposed in his heart that he would not defile himself with the portion of the king's meat, nor with the wine which he drank; for he knew that such a diet would not strengthen his physical powers or increase his mental capability. He would not use wine, nor any other unnatural stimulant; he would do nothing to becloud his mind; and God gave him "knowledge and skill in all learning and wisdom," and also "understanding in all visions and dreams."*

* Dan. 1 : 17.

In later years the cares of state were heavy upon him, he was taxed to the utmost of his capacity; but he grew strong in the conflict with difficulties. He held fast by the hand of Infinite Strength, and would not be overcome. He knew that in order to do his work well, he must have help from God. He realized that amid his trials and persecutions he could not walk apart from God one hour. He prayed three times a day, and God answered his prayers. Daniel's purpose was known to the heavenly Watcher, and as Daniel placed himself on the side of God, to keep his ways, the Lord placed himself on Daniel's side, to keep him.

Daniel's parents had trained him in his childhood to habits of strict temperance. They had taught him that he must conform to nature's laws in all his habits; that his eating and drinking had a direct influence upon his physical, mental, and moral nature, and that he was accountable to God for his capabilities; for he held them all as a gift from God, and must not, by any course of action, dwarf or cripple them. As the result of this teaching, the law of God was exalted in his mind, and reverenced in his heart. During the early years of his captivity, Daniel was passing through an ordeal which was to familiarize him with courtly grandeur, with hypocrisy, and with paganism. A strange school indeed to fit him for a life of sobriety, industry, and faithfulness! And yet he lived uncorrupted by the atmosphere of evil with which he was surrounded.

The experience of Daniel and his youthful companions illustrates the benefits that may result from an abstemious diet, and shows what God will do for those who will co-operate with him in the purifying and uplifting of the soul. They were an honor to God, and a bright and shining light in the court of Babylon.

In this history we hear the voice of God addressing us individually, bidding us gather up all the precious rays of light upon this subject of Christian temperance, and place ourselves in right relation to the laws of health.

We want a share in the eternal inheritance. We want a place in the city of God, free from every impurity. All heaven is watching to see how we are fighting the battle against temptation. Let all who profess the name of Christ so walk before the world that they may teach by example as well as precept the principles of true living. "I beseech you therefore, brethren, by the mercies of God, that ye present your bodies a living sacrifice, holy, acceptable unto God, which is your reasonable service."

EFFECTS OF STIMULANTS.

"KNOW ye not that they which run in a race run all, but one receiveth the prize? So run, that ye may obtain. And every man that striveth for the mastery is temperate in all things. Now they do it to obtain a corruptible crown; but we an incorruptible." *

Here the good results of self-control and temperate habits are set forth. The various games instituted among the ancient Greeks in honor of their gods, are presented before us by the apostle Paul to illustrate the spiritual warfare and its reward. Those who were to participate in these games were trained by the most severe discipline. Every indulgence that would tend to weaken the physical powers was forbidden. Luxurious food and wine were prohibited, in order to promote physical vigor, fortitude, and firmness.

To win the prize for which they strove, — a chaplet of perishable flowers, bestowed amid the applause of the multitude, — was considered the highest honor. If so much could be endured, so much self-denial practiced, in the hope of gaining so worthless a prize, which only one at best could obtain, how much greater should be the sacrifice, how much more willing the self-denial, for an incorruptible crown, and for everlasting life!

There is work for us to do — stern, earnest work. All our habits, tastes, and inclinations must be educated in harmony with the laws of life and health. By this means we may secure the very best physical conditions, and have mental clearness to discern between the evil and the good.

In order rightly to understand the subject of temperance, we must consider it from a Bible standpoint; and nowhere can we find a more comprehensive and forcible illustration of true temperance and its attendant blessings,

* 1 Cor. 9 : 24, 25.   (25)

than is afforded by the history of the prophet Daniel and his Hebrew associates in the court of Babylon.

When these youth were selected to be educated in the " learning and the tongue of the Chaldeans," that they might "stand in the king's palace," there was appointed them a daily allowance from the king's table, both of food and wine. " But Daniel purposed in his heart that he would not defile himself with the portion of the king's meat, nor with the wine which he drank." *

The food appointed them would include meats pronounced unclean by the law of Moses. They requested the officer who had them in charge to give them a more simple fare ; but he hesitated, fearing that such rigid abstinence as they proposed would affect their personal appearance unfavorably, and bring himself into disfavor with the king. Daniel pleaded for a ten days' trial. This was granted ; and at the expiration of that time these youth were found to be far more healthy in appearance than were those who had partaken of the king's dainties. Hence the simple "pulse and water" which they at first requested, was thereafter the food of Daniel and his companions.

It was not their own pride or ambition that had brought these young men into the king's court, — into the companionship of those who neither knew nor feared the true God. They were captives in a strange land, and Infinite Wisdom had placed them there. At this trial of their loyalty, they considered their position, with its dangers and difficulties, and then in the fear of God made their decision. Even at the risk of the king's displeasure, they would be true to the religion of their fathers. They obeyed the divine law, both physical and moral, and the blessing of God gave them strength and comeliness and intellectual power.

These youth had received a right education in early life ; and now, when separated from home influences and sacred associations, they honored the instructors of their childhood. With their habits of self-denial were coupled

* See Daniel 1.

earnestness of purpose, diligence, and steadfastness. They were not actuated by pride or unworthy ambition ; but sought to acquit themselves creditably, for the honor of their down-trodden people, and for His glory whose servants they were.

When the ability and acquirements of these youth were tested by the king at the end of the three years of training, none were found like unto Daniel, Hananiah, Mishael, and Azariah. Their keen apprehension, their choice and exact language, their extensive and varied knowledge, testified to the unimpaired strength and vigor of their mental powers. Therefore they stood before the king. "And in all matters of understanding that the king inquired of them, he found them ten times better than all the magicians and astrologers that were in all his realm."

God always honors the right. The most promising youth from all the lands subdued by the great conqueror had been gathered at Babylon, yet amid them all, the Hebrew captives were without a rival. The erect form, the firm, elastic step, the fair countenance, the undimmed senses, the untainted breath, — all were so many certificates of good habits — insignia of the nobility with which nature honors those who are obedient to her laws.

The history of Daniel and his companions has been recorded on the pages of the inspired word, for the benefit of the youth of all succeeding ages. What men have done, men may do. Did those youthful Hebrews stand firm amid great temptations, and bear a noble testimony in favor of true temperance ? — the youth of to-day may bear a similar testimony.

The lesson here presented is one which we would do well to ponder. Our danger is not from scarcity, but from abundance. We are constantly tempted to excess. Those who would preserve their powers unimpaired for the service of God, must observe strict temperance in the use of his bounties, as well as total abstinence from every injurious or debasing indulgence.

The rising generation are surrounded with allurements calculated to tempt the appetite. Especially in our large cities, every form of indulgence is made easy and inviting. Those who, like Daniel, refuse to defile themselves, will reap the reward of their temperate habits. With their greater physical stamina and increased power of endurance, they have a bank of deposit upon which to draw in case of emergency.

Right physical habits promote mental superiority. Intellectual power, physical strength, and longevity depend upon immutable laws. There is no happen-so, no chance, about this matter. Nature's God will not interfere to preserve men from the consequences of violating nature's laws. There is much sterling truth in the adage, "Every man is the architect of his own fortune." While parents are responsible for the stamp of character, as well as for the education and training, of their sons and daughters, it is still true that our position and usefulness in the world depend, to a great degree, upon our own course of action. Daniel and his companions enjoyed the benefits of correct training and education in early life, but these advantages alone would not have made them what they were. The time came when they must act for themselves — when their future depended upon their own course. Then they decided to be true to the lessons given them in childhood. The fear of God, which is the beginning of wisdom, was the foundation of their greatness. His Spirit strengthened every true purpose, every noble resolution.

Intemperance has cursed the world almost from its infancy. Noah's son was so debased by the excessive use of wine that he lost all sense of propriety, and the curse which followed his sin has never been lifted from his descendants.

Nadab and Abihu were men in holy office; but by the use of wine their minds became so clouded that they could not distinguish between sacred and common things. By the offering of "strange fire" they disregarded God's command, and were slain by his judgments.

Alexander found it much easier to subdue kingdoms than to rule his own spirit. After conquering nations, this so-called great man fell through the indulgence of appetite, — a victim of intemperance.

Notwithstanding thousands of years of experience and progress, the same dark blot which stained the first pages of history remains to disfigure our modern civilization. Drunkenness, with all its woes, is found everywhere we go. In spite of the noble efforts of temperance workers, the evil has gained ground. License laws have been enacted, but legal regulation has not stayed its progress, except in comparatively limited territory. Efforts have been made to establish institutions where the victims of intemperance might receive help to overcome their terrible appetite. This is a noble work, but how much wiser, how much more effective, would have been the removal of the cause of all this woe! Considering only the financial aspect of this question, what folly it is to tolerate a business that is making paupers by the thousand! The laws of the land legalize the trade of making drunkards, and then at great expense provide institutions for converting them again into sober men! Can our legislators furnish no better solution of the liquor question?

So long as the sale of liquor is sanctioned by law, the victims of appetite can receive but little benefit through inebriate asylums. They cannot remain there always; they must again take their place in society. The appetite for intoxicating drinks, though it may be subdued, is not wholly destroyed; and when temptation assails them, as it must on every hand, they too often fall an easy prey.

What can be done to press back the inflowing tide of evil? Let laws be enacted and rigidly enforced prohibiting the sale and use of ardent spirits as a beverage. Let every effort be made to encourage the inebriate's return to temperance and virtue. But even more than this is needed to banish the curse of inebriety from our land.

Let the appetite for intoxicating liquors be removed, and the demand for them is at an end.

Only men of strict temperance and integrity should be admitted to our legislative halls, or chosen to preside in our courts of justice. Property, reputation, and even life itself, are insecure when left to the judgment of men who are intemperate and immoral. How many innocent persons have been condemned to death, how many more have been robbed of all their earthly possessions, by the injustice of drinking jurors, lawyers, witnesses, and even judges!

There is need now of men like Daniel to do and dare. A pure heart and a strong, fearless hand are wanted in the world to-day. God designed that man should be constantly improving, — daily reaching a higher point in the scale of excellence. He will help us, if we seek to help ourselves. It is the duty of every Christian to see that his example and influence are on the side of reform. Let ministers of the gospel lift up their voice like a trumpet, and show the people their transgression, and the house of Israel their sins. The youth need to be instructed. Our hope of happiness in two worlds depends upon our improvement of one. We should be guarded at every point against the first approach to intemperance. If we would preserve our children from evil, we must give them a right example, and then teach them to make God their fear, their wisdom, and their strength.

The use of intoxicating liquor dethrones reason, and hardens the heart against every pure and holy influence. The inanimate rocks will sooner listen to the appeals of truth and justice than will that man whose sensibilities are paralyzed by intemperance. Those who venture to enter the forbidden path are gradually and unconsciously led on, until they become demoralized, corrupted, and maddened. And while Christians are asleep, this evil is gaining more strength and making fresh victims. If the moral sensibilities of Christians were aroused upon the subject of temperance in *all things*, and they realized that the final destiny of every one depends upon the habits he forms, they could, by their example, help those who are weak in self-control, to resist the cravings of appetite.

We witness great struggles in our country to put down intemperance; but it is a hard matter to overcome and chain a full-grown lion. If half the efforts that have been put forth to stay this giant evil had been directed toward enlightening parents in regard to their responsibility in forming the habits and character of their children, a thousand-fold more good might have resulted. The unnatural appetite for spirituous liquors is often created at home, in many cases at the tables of the very ones who are most zealous to lead out in the temperance work. We bid all workers Godspeed; but we invite them to look more deeply into the cause of the evil they war against, and to be more thorough and consistent in reform.

Through the intemperance begun at home, the digestive organs first become weakened, and soon ordinary food does not satisfy the appetite. Unhealthy conditions are established, and there is a craving for more stimulating food. Tea and coffee produce an immediate effect. Under the influence of these poisons the nervous system is excited, and in some cases, for the time being, the intellect seems to be invigorated, the imagination more vivid. Because these stimulants produce such agreeable results, many conclude that they really need them; but there is always a reaction. The nervous system has borrowed power from its future resources for present use, and all this temporary invigoration is followed by a corresponding depression. The suddenness of the relief obtained from tea and coffee, is an evidence that what seems to be strength is only nervous excitement, and consequently must be an injury to the system.

The appetite thus educated to crave continually something stronger, demands an increase of the agreeable excitement. Its demands become more frequent, and more difficult to control. The more debilitated the system and the less able to do without unnatural stimulus, the more the desire for these things increases, until the will is over-borne, and there seems to be no power to deny the unnatural craving.

When there has been a departure from the right path, it is difficult to return. Barriers have been broken down, safeguards removed. One step in the wrong direction prepares the way for another. The least deviation from right principles will lead to separation from God, and may end in destruction. What we do once we more readily do again; and to go forward in a certain path, be it right or wrong, is more easy than to start. To corrupt our ways before God requires no effort; but to engraft habits of righteousness and truth upon the character takes time and patient endeavor.

Many who would hesitate to place liquor to a neighbor's lips, will engage in the raising of hops, and thus lend their influence against the temperance cause. I cannot see how, in the light of the law of God, Christians can conscientiously engage in the raising of hops or in the manufacture of wine and cider for the market.

I have often heard people say, "Oh! this is only sweet cider. It is perfectly harmless, and even healthful." Several quarts, perhaps gallons, are carried home. For a few days it is sweet; then fermentation begins. The sharp taste makes it all the more acceptable to many palates, and the lover of sweet wine and cider is loth to admit that his favorite beverage ever becomes hard and sour.

Intoxication is just as really produced by wine and cider as by stronger drinks, and it is the worst kind of inebriation. The passions are more perverse; the transformation of character is greater, more determined and obstinate. A few quarts of cider or wine may awaken a taste for stronger drinks, and in many cases those who have become confirmed drunkards have thus laid the foundation of the drinking habit.

For persons who have inherited an appetite for stimulants, it is by no means safe to have wine or cider in the house; for Satan is continually soliciting them to indulge. If they yield to his temptations, they do not know where to stop; appetite clamors for indulgence, and is gratified to their ruin. The brain is clouded; reason no longer holds the reins, but lays them on the neck of lust. Licentiousness abounds, and vices of almost every type are practiced as the result of indulging the appetite for wine and cider. It is impossible for one who loves these stimulants, and accustoms himself to their use, to grow in grace. He becomes gross and sensual; the animal passions control the higher powers of the mind, and virtue is not cherished.

Moderate drinking is the school in which men are receiving an education for the drunkard's career. So gradually does Satan lead away from the strongholds of temperance, so insidiously do wine and cider exert their influence upon the taste, that the highway to drunkenness is entered upon all unsuspectingly. The taste for stimulants is cultivated; the nervous system is disordered; Satan keeps the mind in a fever of unrest; and the poor victim, imagining himself perfectly secure, goes on and on, until every barrier is broken down, every principle sacrificed. The strongest resolutions are undermined, and eternal interests are too weak to keep the debased appetite under the control of reason. Some are never really drunk, but are always under the influence of mild intoxicants. They are feverish, unstable in mind, not really delirious, but as truly unbalanced; for the nobler powers of the mind are perverted.

Wherever we go, we encounter the tobacco devotee, enfeebling both mind and body by his darling indulgence. Have men a right to deprive their Maker and the world of the service which is their due? Tobacco is a slow, insidious poison. Its effects are more difficult to cleanse from the system than are those of liquor. It binds the victim in even stronger bands of slavery than does the intoxicating cup. It is a disgusting habit, defiling to the user, and very annoying to others. We rarely pass through a crowd but men will puff their poisoned breath in our faces. It is unpleasant, if not dangerous, to remain in a railway car or in a room where the atmosphere is impregnated with the fumes of liquor and tobacco. Is it honest thus to contaminate the air which others must breathe?

What power can the tobacco devotee have to stay the progress of intemperance? There must be a revolution upon the subject of tobacco before the ax will be laid at the root of the tree. Tea, coffee, and tobacco, as well as alcoholic drinks, are different degrees in the scale of artificial stimulants.

The effect of tea and coffee, as heretofore shown, tends in the same direction as that of wine and cider, liquor and tobacco.

Tea is a stimulant, and to a certain extent produces intoxication. It gradually impairs the energy of body and mind. Its first effect is exhilarating, because it quickens the motions of the living machinery; and the tea-drinker thinks that it is doing him great service. But this is a mistake. When its influence is gone, the unnatural force abates, and the result is languor and debility corresponding to the artificial vivacity imparted. The second effect of tea-drinking is headache, wakefulness, palpitation of the heart, indigestion, trembling, and many other evils.

Coffee is a hurtful indulgence. It temporarily excites the mind to unwonted action, but the after-effect is exhaustion, prostration, paralysis of the mental, moral, and physical powers. The mind becomes enervated, and unless through determined effort the habit is overcome, the activity of the brain is permanently lessened.

All these nerve irritants are wearing away the life-forces, and the restlessness caused by shattered nerves, the impatience, the mental feebleness, become a warring element, antagonizing to spiritual progress. Then should not those who advocate temperance and reform be awake to counteract the evils of these injurious drinks? In some cases it is as difficult to break up the tea-and-coffee habit as it is for the inebriate to discontinue the use of liquor. The money expended for tea and coffee is worse than wasted. They do the user only harm, and that continually. Those who use tea, coffee, opium, and alcohol, may sometimes live to old age, but this fact is no argument in favor of the use of these stimulants. What these persons might have accomplished, but failed to do because of their intemperate habits, the great day of God alone will reveal.

Those who resort to tea and coffee for stimulation to labor, will feel the evil effects of this course in trembling nerves and lack of self-control. Tired nerves need rest and quiet. Nature needs time to recuperate her exhausted energies. But if her forces are goaded on by the use of stimulants, there is, whenever this process is repeated, a lessening of real force. For a time more may be accomplished under the unnatural stimulus, but gradually it becomes more difficult to rouse the energies to the desired point, and at last exhausted nature can no longer respond.

The habit of drinking tea and coffee is a greater evil than is often suspected. Many who have accustomed themselves to the use of stimulating drinks, suffer from headache and nervous prostration, and lose much time on account of sickness. They imagine they cannot live without the stimulus, and are ignorant of its effect upon health. What makes it the more dangerous is, that its evil effects are so often attributed to other causes.

Through the use of stimulants, the whole system suffers. The nerves are unbalanced, the liver is morbid in its action, the quality and circulation of the blood are affected, and the skin becomes inactive and sallow. The mind, too, is injured. The immediate influence of these stimulants is to excite the brain to undue activity, only to leave it weaker and less capable of exertion. The after-effect is prostration, not only mental and physical, but moral. As a result we see nervous men and women, of unsound judgment and unbalanced mind. They often manifest a hasty, impatient, accusing spirit, viewing the faults of others as through a magnifying glass, and utterly unable to discern their own defects.

When these tea and coffee users meet together for social entertainment, the effects of their pernicious habit are manifest. All partake freely of the favorite beverages, and as the stimulating influence is felt, their tongues are loosened, and they begin the wicked work of talking against others. Their words are not few or well chosen. The tid-bits of gossip are passed around, too often the poison of scandal as well. These thoughtless gossipers forget that they have a witness. An unseen Watcher is writing their words in the books of heaven. All these unkind criticisms, these exaggerated reports, these envious feelings, expressed under the excitement of the cup of tea, Jesus registers as against himself. "Inasmuch as ye have done it unto one of the least of these my brethren, ye have done it unto me." *

We are already suffering because of the wrong habits of our fathers, and yet how many take a course in every way worse than theirs! Opium, tea, coffee, tobacco, and liquor are rapidly extinguishing the spark of vitality still left in the race. Every year millions of gallons of intoxicating liquors are drank, and millions of dollars are spent for tobacco. And the slaves of appetite, while constantly spending their earnings in sensual indulgence, rob their children of food and clothing and the advantages of education. There can never be a right state of society while these evils exist.

When the appetite for spirituous liquor is indulged, the man voluntarily places to his lips the draught which debases below the level of the brute, him who was made in the image of God. Reason is paralyzed, the intellect is benumbed, the animal passions are excited, and then follow crimes of the most debasing character. How can the user of rum or tobacco give to God an undivided heart? It is impossible. Neither can he love his neighbor as himself. The darling indulgence engrosses all his affections. To gratify his craving for strong drink, he sells reason

* Matt. 25:40.

and self-control. He places to his lips that which stupefies the brain, paralyzes the intellect, and makes him a shame and curse to his family, and a terror to all around him. If men would become temperate in all things, if they would touch not, taste not, handle not, tea, coffee, tobacco, wines, opium, and alcoholic drinks, reason would take the reins of government in her own hands, and hold the appetites and passions under control.

Through appetite, Satan controls the mind and the whole being. Thousands who might have lived, have passed into the grave, physical, mental, and moral wrecks, because they sacrificed all their powers to the indulgence of appetite. The necessity for the men of this generation to call to their aid the power of the will, strengthened by the grace of God, in order to withstand the temptations of Satan, and resist the least indulgence of perverted appetite, is far greater than it was several generations ago. But the present generation have less power of self-control than had those who lived then. Those who indulged in these stimulants transmitted their depraved appetites and passions to their children, and greater moral power is now required to resist intemperance in all its forms. The only perfectly safe course is to stand firm, observing strict temperance in all things, and never venturing into the path of danger.

I feel an intense interest that fathers and mothers should realize the solemn obligations that are resting upon them at this time. We are bringing up children who will be controlled by the power of Satan or by that of Christ. The only way in which any can be secure against the power of intemperance, is to abstain wholly from wine, beer, and strong drinks. We must teach our children that in order to be manly they must let these things alone. God has shown us what constitutes true manliness. It is he that overcometh who will be honored, and whose name will not be blotted out of the book of life.

When the Lord would raise up Samson as a deliverer of his people, he enjoined upon the mother correct habits

of life before the birth of her child. And the same prohibition was to be imposed, from the first, upon the child;
for he was to be consecrated to God as a Nazarite from
his birth.

The angel of God appeared to the wife of Manoah,
and informed her that she should have a son; and in view
of this he gave her the important directions: "Now therefore beware, I pray thee, and drink not wine nor strong
drink, and eat not any unclean thing." *

God had important work for the promised child of Manoah to do, and it was to secure for him the qualifications necessary for this work, that the habits of both the
mother and the child were to be so carefully regulated.
"Neither let her drink wine nor strong drink," was the
angel's instruction for the wife of Manoah, "nor eat any
unclean thing; all that I commanded her let her observe." The child will be affected for good or evil by
the habits of the mother. She must herself be controlled
by principle, and must practice temperance and self-denial,
if she would seek the welfare of her child.

In the New Testament we find a no less impressive
example of the importance of temperate habits.

John the Baptist was a reformer. To him was committed a great work for the people of his time. And in
preparation for that work, all his habits were carefully
regulated, even from his birth. The angel Gabriel was
sent from heaven to instruct the parents of John in the
principles of health reform. He "shall drink neither wine
nor strong drink," said the heavenly messenger; "and he
shall be filled with the Holy Ghost." †

John separated himself from his friends, and from the
luxuries of life, dwelling alone in the wilderness, and sub-
sisting upon a purely vegetable diet. The simplicity of
his dress — a garment woven of camel's hair — was a rebuke to the extravagance and display of the people of
his generation, especially of the Jewish priests. His diet
also, of locusts and wild honey, was a rebuke to the
gluttony that everywhere prevailed.

* Judges 13 : 4, 14.   † Luke 1 : 15.

The work of John was foretold by the prophet Malachi: "Behold, I will send you Elijah the prophet before the coming of the great and dreadful day of the Lord; and he shall turn the heart of the fathers to the children, and the heart of the children to their fathers."* John the Baptist went forth in the spirit and power of Elijah, to prepare the way of the Lord, and to turn the people to the wisdom of the just. He was a representative of those living in the last days, to whom God has intrusted sacred truths to present before the people, to prepare the way for the second appearing of Christ. And the same principles of temperance which John practiced should be observed by those who in our day are to warn the world of the coming of the Son of man.

God has made man in his own image, and he expects man to preserve unimpaired the powers that have been imparted to him for the Creator's service. Then should we not heed his admonitions, and seek to preserve every power in the best condition to serve him? The very best we can give to God is feeble enough.

Why is there so much misery in the world to-day? Is it because God loves to see his creatures suffer?—O no! it is because men have become weakened by immoral practices. We mourn over Adam's transgression, and seem to think that our first parents showed great weakness in yielding to temptation; but if Adam's transgression were the only evil we had to meet, the condition of the world would be much better than it is. There has been a succession of falls since Adam's day.

Indulgence in spirituous liquors is causing great wretchedness in the world. Though liquor drinkers are told again and again that they are shortening their life, they still go on in transgression. Why not cease to break the laws of God? Why not seek to preserve themselves in a condition of health? This is what God requires of them. If Christians would bring all their appetites and passions under the control of enlightened conscience, feeling it a duty they owe to God and to their neighbor to obey the laws

* Mal. 4 : 5, 6.

which govern life and health, they would have the blessing of physical and mental vigor; they would have moral power to engage in the warfare against Satan; and in the name of Him who conquered in their behalf, they might be more than conquerors on their own account.

All around us are the victims of depraved appetite, and what are you going to do for them? Can you not, by your example, help them to place their feet in the path of temperance? Can you have a sense of the temptations that are coming upon the youth who are growing up around us, and not seek to warn and save them? Who will stand on the Lord's side? Who will help to press back this tide of immorality, of woe and wretchedness, that is filling the world? We entreat of you to turn your attention to the work of overcoming. Those who shall at last have a right to the tree of life, will be those who have kept God's commandments.

It is not an easy matter to overcome the appetite for narcotics and stimulants. But in the name of Christ this great victory can be gained. His love for the fallen race was so great that he made an infinite sacrifice to reach them in their degradation, and through his divine power finally elevate them to his throne. But it rests with man whether Christ shall accomplish for him that which he is fully able to do. God cannot work against man's will to save him from Satan's artifices. Man must put forth his human power to resist and conquer at any cost; he must be a co-worker with Christ. Then, through the victory that it is his privilege to gain by the all-powerful name of Jesus, he may become an heir of God, and a partaker with Christ of his glory. No drunkard can inherit the kingdom of God; but "to him that overcometh will I grant to sit with me in my throne, even as I also overcame, and am set down with my Father in his throne." *

* Rev. 3 : 21.

RELATION OF DIET TO HEALTH
AND MORALS.

ONLY one lease of life is granted us; and the inquiry with every one should be, "How can I invest my powers so that they may yield the greatest profit? How can I do most for the glory of God and the benefit of my fellow-men?" For life is valuable only as it is used for the attainment of these ends.

Our first duty toward God and our fellow-beings is that of self-development. Every faculty with which the Creator has endowed us should be cultivated to the highest degree of perfection, that we may be able to do the greatest amount of good of which we are capable. Hence that time is spent to good account which is used in the establishment and preservation of physical and mental health. We cannot afford to dwarf or cripple any function of body or mind. As surely as we do this, we must suffer the consequences.

Every man has the opportunity, to a great extent, of making himself whatever he chooses to be. The blessings of this life, and also of the immortal state, are within his reach. He may build up a character of solid worth, gaining new strength at every step. He may advance daily in knowledge and wisdom, conscious of new delights as he progresses, adding virtue to virtue, grace to grace. His faculties will improve by use; the more wisdom he gains, the greater will be his capacity for acquiring. His intelligence, knowledge, and virtue will thus develop into greater strength and more perfect symmetry.

On the other hand, he may allow his powers to rust out for want of use, or to be perverted through evil habits, lack of self-control or moral and religious stamina. His course then tends downward; he is disobedient to the law of God and to the laws of health. Appetite conquers him; inclination carries him away. It is easier for him to allow the powers of evil, which are always active, to drag him backward, than to struggle against them, and go forward. Dissipation, disease, and death follow. This is the history of many lives that might have been useful in the cause of God and humanity.

One of the strongest temptations that man has to meet is upon the point of appetite. In the beginning the Lord made man upright. He was created with a perfectly balanced mind, the size and strength of all his organs being fully and harmoniously developed. But through the seductions of the wily foe, the prohibition of God was disregarded, and the laws of nature wrought out their full penalty.

Adam and Eve were permitted to eat of all the trees in their Eden home, save one. The Lord said to the holy pair, "In the day that ye eat of the tree of knowledge of good and evil, ye shall surely die." * Eve was beguiled by the serpent, and made to believe that God would not do as he had said. She ate, and thinking she felt the sensation of a new and more exalted life, she bore the fruit to her husband. The serpent had said that she should not die, and she felt no ill effects from eating the fruit, — nothing which could be interpreted to mean death, but, instead, a pleasurable sensation, which she imagined was as the angels felt. Her experience stood arrayed against the positive command of Jehovah, yet Adam permitted himself to be seduced by it.

Thus we often find it, even in the religious world. God's express commands are transgressed ; and "because sentence against an evil work is not executed speedily, therefore the heart of the sons of men is fully set in them to do evil." † In the face of the most positive commands of God, men and women will follow their own inclinations, and then dare to pray over the matter, to prevail upon God to allow them to go contrary to his expressed will. Satan comes to the side of such persons, as he did to Eve in Eden, and impresses them. They have an exercise of mind, and this they relate as a most wonderful

* See Genesis 3.　　† Eccl. 8 : 11.

experience which the Lord has given them. But true experience will be in harmony with natural and divine law; false experience arrays itself against the laws of life and the precepts of Jehovah.

Since the first surrender to appetite, mankind have been growing more and more self-indulgent, until health has been sacrificed on the altar of appetite. The inhabitants of the antediluvian world were intemperate in eating and drinking. They would have flesh-meats, although God had at that time given man no permission to eat animal food. They ate and drank till the indulgence of their depraved appetite knew no bounds, and they became so corrupt that God could bear with them no longer. Their cup of iniquity was full, and he cleansed the earth of its moral pollution by a flood.

As men multiplied upon the earth after the flood, they again forgot God, and corrupted their ways before him. Intemperance in every form increased, until almost the whole world was given up to its sway. Entire cities have been swept from the face of the earth because of the debasing crimes and revolting iniquity that made them a blot upon the fair field of God's created works. The gratification of unnatural appetite led to the sins that caused the destruction of Sodom and Gomorrah. God ascribes the fall of Babylon to her gluttony and drunkenness. Indulgence of appetite and passion was the foundation of all their sins.

Esau had a strong desire for a particular article of food, and he had so long gratified himself that he did not feel the necessity of turning from the tempting, coveted dish. He allowed his imagination to dwell upon it until the power of appetite bore down every other consideration, and controlled him. He thought he would suffer great inconvenience, and even death, if he could not have that particular dish. The more he reflected upon it, the more his desire strengthened, until his birthright lost its value and sacredness in his sight, and he bartered it away. He flattered himself that he could dispose of his birthright at will, and buy it back at pleasure; but when he sought to regain it, even at a great sacrifice, he was not able to do so. He then bitterly repented of his rashness, his folly, his madness; but it was all in vain. He had despised the blessing, and the Lord had removed it from him forever.

When the God of Israel brought his people out of Egypt, he withheld flesh-meats from them in a great measure, but gave them bread from heaven, and water from the flinty rock. With this they were not satisfied. They loathed the food given them, and wished themselves back in Egypt, where they could sit by the flesh-pots. They preferred to endure slavery, and even death, rather than to be deprived of flesh. God granted their desire, giving them flesh, and leaving them to eat till their gluttony produced a plague, from which many of them died.

Example after example might be cited to show the effects of yielding to appetite. It seemed a small matter to our first parents to transgress the command of God in that one act, — the eating from a tree that was so beautiful to the sight and so pleasant to the taste, — put it broke their allegiance to God, and opened the gates to a flood of guilt and woe that has deluged the world.

Crime and disease have increased with every succeeding generation. Intemperance in eating and drinking, and the indulgence of the baser passions, have benumbed the nobler faculties of man. Reason, instead of being the ruler, has come to be the slave of appetite to an alarming extent. An increasing desire for rich food has been indulged, until it has become the fashion to crowd all the delicacies possible into the stomach. Especially at parties of pleasure is the appetite indulged with but little restraint. Rich dinners and late suppers are served, consisting of highly seasoned meats, with rich sauces, cakes, pies, ices, tea, coffee, etc. No wonder that, with such a diet, people have sallow complexions, and suffer untold agonies from dyspepsia.

Against every transgression of the laws of life, nature

will utter her protest. She bears abuse as long as she can; but finally the retribution comes, and it falls upon the mental as well as the physical powers. Nor does it end with the transgressor; the effects of his indulgence are seen in his offspring, and thus the evil is passed down from generation to generation.

The youth of to-day are a sure index to the future of society; and as we view them, what can we hope for that future? The majority are fond of amusement and averse to work. They lack moral courage to deny self and to respond to the claims of duty. They have but little self-control, and become excited and angry on the slightest occasion. Very many in every age and station of life are without principle or conscience; and with their idle, spendthrift habits they are rushing into vice and are corrupting society, until our world is becoming a second Sodom. If the appetites and passions were under the control of reason and religion, society would present a widely different aspect. God never designed that the present woeful condition of things should exist; it has been brought about through the gross violation of nature's laws.

The character is formed, to a great extent, in early years. The habits then established have more influence than any natural endowment, in making men either giants or dwarfs in intellect; for the very best talents may, through wrong habits, become warped and enfeebled. The earlier in life one contracts hurtful habits, the more firmly will they hold their victim in slavery, and the more certainly will they lower his standard of spirituality. On the other hand, if correct and virtuous habits are formed in youth, they will generally mark the course of the possessor through life. In most cases, it will be found that those who in later life reverence God and honor the right, learned that lesson before there was time for the world to stamp its images of sin upon the soul. Those of mature age are generally as insensible to new impressions as is the hardened rock; but youth is impressible. Youth is the time to acquire knowledge for daily practice through

life ; a right character may then be easily formed. It is
the time to establish good habits, to gain and to hold
the power of self-control. Youth is the sowing time, and
the seed sown determines the harvest, both for this life
and the life to come.

Parents should make it their first object to become intelligent in regard to the proper manner of dealing with
their children, that they may secure to them sound minds
in sound bodies. The principles of temperance should be
carried out in all the details of home life. Self-denial
should be taught to children, and enforced upon them,
so far as consistent, from babyhood. Teach the little
ones that they should eat to live, not live to eat ; that
appetite must be held in abeyance to the will ; and that
the will must be governed by calm, intelligent reason.

If parents have transmitted to their children tendencies which will make more difficult the work of educating
them to be strictly temperate, and of cultivating pure and
virtuous habits, what a solemn responsibility rests upon
the parents to counteract that influence by every means
in their power ! How diligently and earnestly should they
strive to do their duty by their unfortunate offspring ! To
parents is committed the sacred trust of guarding the physical and moral constitution of their children. Those who
indulge a child's appetite, and do not teach him to control his passions, may afterward see, in the tobacco-lov-
ing, liquor-drinking slave, whose senses are benumbed,
and whose lips utter falsehood and profanity, the terrible
mistake they have made.

It is impossible for those who give the reins to appetite to attain to Christian perfection. The moral sensibilities of your children cannot be easily aroused, unless
you are careful in the selection of their food. Many a
mother sets a table that is a snare to her family. Flesh-
meats, butter, cheese, rich pastry, spiced foods, and condiments are freely partaken of by both old and young.
These things do their work in deranging the stomach, exciting the nerves, and enfeebling the intellect. The blood-

making organs cannot convert such things into good blood. The grease cooked in the food renders it difficult of digestion. The effect of cheese is deleterious. Fine-flour bread does not impart to the system the nourishment that is to be found in unbolted wheat bread. Its common use will not keep the system in the best condition. Spices at first irritate the tender coating of the stomach, but finally destroy the natural sensitiveness of this delicate membrane. The blood becomes fevered, the animal propensities are aroused, while the moral and intellectual powers are weakened, and become servants to the baser passions. The mother should study to set a simple yet nutritious diet before her family.

God has furnished man with abundant means for the gratification of an unperverted appetite. He has spread before him the products of the earth, — a bountiful variety of food that is palatable to the taste and nutritious to the system. Of these our benevolent heavenly Father says we may freely eat. Fruits, grains, and vegetables, prepared in a simple way, free from spice and grease of all kinds, make, with milk or cream, the most healthful diet. They impart nourishment to the body, and give a power of endurance and a vigor of intellect that are not produced by a stimulating diet.

Those who use flesh-meats freely, do not always have an unclouded brain and an active intellect, because the use of the flesh of animals tends to cause a grossness of body, and to benumb the finer sensibilities of the mind. The liability to disease is increased by flesh-eating. We do not hesitate to say that meat is not essential to the maintenance of health and strength.

Those who subsist largely upon meat, cannot avoid sometimes eating flesh which is more or less diseased. In many cases the process of fitting animals for market produces an unhealthy condition. Shut away from light and pure air, inhaling the atmosphere of filthy stables, the entire body soon becomes contaminated with foul matter; and when such flesh is received into the

human body, it corrupts the blood, and disease is produced. If the person already has impure blood, this unhealthful condition will be greatly aggravated. But few
can be made to believe that it is the meat they have
eaten which has poisoned their blood and caused their suffering. Many die of diseases wholly due to meat-eating,
when the real cause is scarcely suspected by themselves
or others. Some do not immediately feel its effects, but
this is no evidence that it does not hurt them. It may
be doing its work surely upon the system, yet for the
time being the victim may realize nothing of it.

Pork, although one of the most common articles of diet,
is one of the most injurious. God did not prohibit the
Hebrews from eating swine's flesh merely to show his
authority, but because it is not a proper article of food for
man. God never created the swine to be eaten under any
circumstances. It is impossible for the flesh of any living
creature to be healthful when filth is its natural element,
and when it feeds upon every detestable thing.

It is not the chief end of man to gratify his appetite.
There are physical wants to be supplied ; but because of
this is it necessary that man shall be controlled by appetite ? Will the people who are seeking to become holy, pure,
refined, that they may be introduced into the society of
heavenly angels, continue to take the life of God's creatures,
and enjoy their flesh as a luxury ? From what the Lord
has shown me, this order of things will be changed, and
God's peculiar people will exercise temperance in all things.

There is a class who seem to think that whatever is
eaten is lost, that anything tossed into the stomach to fill
it, will do as well as food prepared with intelligence and
care. But it is important that we relish the food we eat.
If we cannot, and have to eat mechanically, we fail to
receive the proper nourishment. Our bodies are constructed from what we eat ; and in order to make tissues
of good quality, we must have the right kind of food,
and it must be prepared with such skill as will best adapt
it to the wants of the system. It is a religious duty for

those who cook, to learn how to prepare healthful food in a variety of ways, so that it may be both palatable and healthful. Poor cookery is wearing away the life energies of thousands. More souls are lost from this cause than many realize. It deranges the system and produces disease. In the condition thus induced, heavenly things cannot be readily discerned.

Some do not feel that it is a religious duty to prepare food properly; hence they do not try to learn how. They let the bread sour before baking, and the saleratus added to remedy the cook's carelessness, makes it totally unfit for the human stomach. It requires thought and care to make good bread. But there is more religion in a good loaf of bread than many think. Food can be prepared simply and healthfully, but it requires skill to make it both palatable and nourishing. In order to learn how to cook, women should study, and then patiently reduce what they learn to practice. People are suffering because they will not take the trouble to do this. I say to such, It is time for you to rouse your dormant energies, and inform yourselves. Do not think the time wasted which is devoted to obtaining a thorough knowledge and experience in the preparation of healthful, palatable food. No matter how long an experience you have had in cooking, if you still have the responsibilities of a family, it is your duty to learn how to care for them properly. If necessary, go to some good cook, and put yourself under her instruction until you are mistress of the art.

A wrong course of eating or drinking destroys health, and with it the sweetness of life. O, how many times has a good meal, as it is called, been purchased at the expense of sleep and quiet rest! Thousands, by indulging a perverted appetite, have brought on fever or some other acute disease, which has resulted in death. That was enjoyment purchased at an immense cost.

Because it is wrong to eat merely to gratify a perverted taste, it does not follow that we should be indifferent in regard to our food. It is a matter of the highest importance. No one should adopt an impoverished diet. Many are debilitated from disease, and need nourishing, well-cooked food. Health reformers, above all others, should be careful to avoid extremes. The body must have sufficient nourishment. The God who gives his beloved sleep has furnished them also suitable food to sustain the physical system in a healthy condition.

Many turn from light and knowledge, and sacrifice principle to taste. They eat when the system needs no food, and at irregular intervals, because they have no moral stamina to resist inclination. As the result, the abused stomach rebels, and suffering follows. Regularity in eating is very important for health of body and serenity of mind. Never should a morsel of food pass the lips between meals.

Many indulge in the pernicious habit of eating just before retiring. They may have taken their regular meals, yet because they feel a sense of faintness, they think they must have a lunch. By indulging this wrong practice it becomes a habit, and they feel as though they could not sleep without food. In many cases this faintness comes because the digestive organs have been too severely taxed through the day in disposing of the great quantities of food forced upon them. These organs need a period of entire rest from labor, to recover their exhausted energies. A second meal should never be eaten until the stomach has had time to recover from the labor of digesting the preceding meal. When we lie down at night, the stomach should have its work all done, that it, as well as other portions of the body, may enjoy rest. But if more food is forced upon it, the digestive organs are put in motion again, to perform the same round of labor through the sleeping hours. The sleep of such is often disturbed with unpleasant dreams, and in the morning they awake unrefreshed. When this practice is followed, the digestive organs lose their natural vigor, and the person finds himself a miserable dyspeptic. And not only does the transgression of nature's laws affect the individual unfavorably, but others suffer more or less with him. Let any one take a course that irritates him in any way, and see how quickly he manifests impatience! He cannot, without special grace, speak or act calmly. He casts a shadow wherever he goes. How can any one say, then, " It is nobody's business what I eat or drink"?

It is possible to eat immoderately, even of wholesome food. It does not follow that because one has discarded the use of hurtful articles of diet, he can eat just as much as he pleases. Overeating, no matter what the quality of the food, clogs the living machine, and thus hinders it in its work.

Many make a mistake in drinking cold water with their meals. Food should not be washed down. Taken with meals, water diminishes the flow of the saliva; and the colder the water, the greater the injury to the stomach. Ice-water or ice-lemonade, taken with meals, will arrest digestion until the system has imparted sufficient warmth to the stomach to enable it to take up its work again. Masticate slowly, and allow the saliva to mingle with the food.

The more liquid there is taken into the stomach with the meals, the more difficult it is for the food to digest; for the liquid must first be absorbed. Do not eat largely of salt; give up spiced pickles; keep fiery food out of the stomach; eat fruit with the meals, and the irritation that calls for so much drink will cease to exist. But if anything is needed to quench thirst, pure water is all that nature requires. Never take tea, coffee, beer, wine, or any spirituous liquor.

In order to secure healthy digestion, food should be eaten slowly. Those who wish to avoid dyspepsia, and those who realize their obligation to keep all their powers in a condition which will enable them to render the best service to God, will do well to remember this. If your time to eat is limited, do not bolt your food, but eat less, and masticate slowly. The benefit derived from food does not depend so much on the quantity eaten, as on its

thorough digestion; nor the gratification of taste so much
on the amount of food swallowed, as on the length of
time it remains in the mouth. Those who are excited,
anxious, or in a hurry, would do well not to eat until they
have found rest or relief; for the vital powers, already
severely taxed, cannot supply the necessary digestive
fluids. When traveling, some are almost constantly nib-
bling, if there is anything within their reach. This is a
most pernicious practice. If travelers would eat regularly
of the simplest and most nutritious kinds of food, they
would not experience so great weariness, nor suffer so
much from sickness.

In order to preserve health, temperance in all things is
necessary, — temperance in labor, temperance in eating
and drinking. Our heavenly Father sent the light of
health reform to guard against the evils resulting from a
debased appetite, that those who love purity and holiness
may know how to use with discretion the good things he
has provided for them, and that by exercising temperance
in daily life, they may be sanctified through the truth.

At general meetings and camp-meetings we should
have good, wholesome, nourishing food, prepared in a simple manner. We should not turn these seasons into occasions for feasting. If we appreciate the blessings of God,
if we are feeding on the bread of life, we will not be much
concerned about gratifying the appetite. The great burden of our thoughts will be, How is it with my soul?
There will be such a longing for spiritual food, — something which will impart spiritual strength, — that we will
not complain if the diet is plain and simple.

God requires the body to be rendered a living sacrifice to him, not a dead or a dying sacrifice. The
offerings of the ancient Hebrews were to be without
blemish, and will it be pleasing to God to accept a human offering that is filled with disease and corruption?
He tells us that our body is the temple of the Holy
Ghost; and he requires us to take care of this temple,
that it may be a fit habitation for his Spirit. The apos-

tle Paul gives us this admonition: "Ye are not your own; for ye are bought with a price; therefore glorify God in your body and in your spirit, which are God's."* All should be very careful to preserve the body in the best condition of health, that they may render to God perfect service, and do their duty in the family and in society.

It is as truly a sin to violate the laws of our being as it is to break the ten commandments. To do either is to break God's laws. Those who transgress the law of God in their physical organism, will be inclined to violate the law of God spoken from Sinai.

Our Saviour warned his disciples that just prior to his second coming a state of things would exist very similar to that which preceded the flood. Eating and drinking would be carried to excess, and the world would be given up to pleasure. This state of things does exist at the present time. The world is largely given up to the indulgence of appetite; and the disposition to follow worldly customs will bring us into bondage to perverted habits, — habits that will make us more and more like the doomed inhabitants of Sodom. I have wondered that the inhabitants of the earth were not destroyed, like the people of Sodom and Gomorrah. I see reason enough for the present state of degeneracy and mortality in the world. Blind passion controls reason, and every high consideration is, with many, sacrificed to lust.

To keep the body in a healthy condition, in order that all parts of the living machinery may act harmoniously, should be a study of our life. The children of God cannot glorify him with sickly bodies or dwarfed minds. Those who indulge in any species of intemperance, either in eating or drinking, waste their physical energies and weaken moral power.

The apostle Peter understood the relation between the mind and the body, and raised his voice in warning to his brethren: "Dearly beloved, I beseech you, as strangers and pilgrims, abstain from fleshly lusts, which war against

* 1 Cor. 6: 19, 20.

the soul." *   Many regard this text as a warning against
licentiousness only ; but it has a broader meaning. It for-
bids every injurious gratification of appetite or passion.
Every perverted appetite becomes a warring lust. Appetite was given us for a good purpose, not to become the minister of death by being perverted, and
thus degenerating into "lusts which war against the soul."
Peter's admonition is a most direct and forcible warning against the use of all stimulants and narcotics. These
indulgences may well be classed among the lusts that
exert a pernicious influence upon moral character.

When Paul wrote, " And the very God of peace sanctify you wholly," †   he did not exhort his brethren to aim
at a standard which it was impossible for them to reach ;
he did not pray that they might have blessings which
it was not the will of God to give. He knew that all
who would be fitted to meet Christ in peace, must possess a pure and holy character.

The strength of the temptation to indulge appetite
can be measured only by the inexpressible anguish of
our Redeemer in that long fast in the wilderness. He
knew that the indulgence of perverted appetite would so
deaden man's perceptions that sacred things could not
be discerned. Adam fell by the indulgence of appetite ;
Christ overcame by the denial of appetite. And our only
hope of regaining Eden is through firm self-control. If
the power of indulged appetite was so strong upon the
race, that, in order to break its hold, the divine Son of
God, in man's behalf, had to endure a fast of nearly six
weeks, what a work is before the Christian ! Yet, however great the struggle, he may overcome. By the help
of that divine power which withstood the fiercest temptations that Satan could invent, he too may be entirely
successful in his warfare with evil, and at last may wear
the victor's crown in the kingdom of God.

EXTREMES IN DIET.

MANY of the views held by Seventh-day Adventists differ widely from those held by the world in general. Those who advocate an unpopular truth should, above all others, seek to be consistent in their own life. They should not try to see how different they can be from others, but how near they can come to those whom they wish to influence, that they may help them to the positions they themselves so highly prize. Such a course will commend the truths they hold.

Those who are advocating a reform in diet should, by the provision they make for their own table, present the advantages of hygiene in the best light. They should so exemplify its principles as to commend it to the judgment of candid minds.

There is a large class who will reject any reform movement, however reasonable, if it lays a restriction upon the appetite. They consult taste, instead of reason and the laws of health. By this class, all who leave the beaten track of custom and advocate reform will be opposed, and accounted radical, let them pursue ever so consistent a course.

But no one should permit opposition or ridicule to turn him from the work of reform, or cause him to lightly regard it. He who is imbued with the spirit which actuated Daniel, will not be narrow or conceited, but he will be firm and decided in standing for the right. In all his associations, whether with his brethren or with others, he will not swerve from principle, while at the same time he will not fail to manifest a noble, Christ-like patience. When those who advocate hygienic reform carry the matter to extremes, people are not to blame if they become disgusted. Too often our religious faith is thus brought into disrepute, and in many cases those who witness such exhibitions of inconsistency can never afterward be brought to think that there is anything good in the reform. These extremists do more harm in a few months than they can undo in a life-time. They are engaged in a work which Satan loves to see go on.

Two classes have been presented before me: first, those who are not living up to the light which God has given them; secondly, those who are too rigid in carrying out their one-sided ideas of reform, and enforcing them on others. When they take a position, they stand to it stubbornly, and carry nearly everything over the mark.

The first class adopted the reform because some one else did. They did not obtain a clear understanding of its principles for themselves. Many of those who profess the truth have received it because some one else did, and for their life they could not give the reason of their faith. This is why they are so unstable. Instead of weighing their motives in the light of eternity, instead of obtaining a practical knowledge of the principles underlying all their actions, instead of digging down to the bottom, and building upon a right foundation for themselves, they are walking in the light of another's torch, and will surely fail.

The other class take wrong views of the reform. They adopt too meager a diet. They subsist upon a poor quality of food, prepared without reference to the nourishment of the system. It is important that food be prepared with care, so that the appetite, when not perverted, can relish it.

Because we, from principle, discard the use of those things which irritate the stomach and destroy health, the idea should never be given that it is of little consequence what we eat. I do not recommend an impoverished diet. Many who need the benefits of healthful living, and from conscientious motives adopt what they believe to be such, are deceived by supposing that a meager bill of fare, prepared without painstaking, and consisting mostly of mushes and so-called gems, heavy and sodden, is what is meant by a reformed diet. Some use milk and a large amount of sugar on mush, thinking that they are carrying out health reform. But the sugar and milk combined are liable to cause fermentation in the stomach, and are thus harmful. The free use of sugar in any form tends to clog the system, and is not unfrequently a cause of disease. Some think that they must eat only just such an amount, and just such a quality, and confine themselves to two or three kinds of food. But in eating too small an amount, and that not of the best quality, they do not receive sufficient nourishment.

There is real common sense in health reform. People cannot all eat the same things. Some articles of food that are wholesome and palatable to one person, may be hurtful to another. Some cannot use milk, while others can subsist upon it. For some, dried beans and peas are wholesome, while others cannot digest them. Some stomachs have become so sensitive that they cannot make use of the coarser kind of graham flour. So it is impossible to make an unvarying rule by which to regulate every one's dietetic habits.

Narrow ideas, an overstraining of small points, have been a great injury to the cause of hygiene. There may be such an effort at economy in the preparation of food, that, instead of a healthful diet, it becomes a poverty-stricken diet. What is the result?—Poverty of the blood. I have seen several cases of disease most difficult to cure, which were due to impoverished diet. The persons thus afflicted were not compelled by poverty to adopt a meager diet, but did so in order to follow out their own erroneous ideas of what constitutes health reform. Day after day, meal after meal, the same articles of food were prepared without variation, until dyspepsia and general debility resulted.

Many who adopt the health reform complain that it

does not agree with them ; but after sitting at their tables I come to the conclusion that it is not the health reform that is at fault, but the poorly prepared food. I appeal to men and women to whom God has given intelligence : learn how to cook. I make no mistake when I say *men*, for they, as well as women, need to understand the simple, healthful preparation of food. Their business often takes them where they cannot obtain wholesome food. They may be called to remain days and even weeks in families that are entirely ignorant in this respect. Then, if they have the knowledge, they can use it to good purpose.

Investigate your habits of diet. Study from cause to effect, but do not bear false witness against health reform by ignorantly pursuing a course which militates against it. Do not neglect or abuse the body, and thus unfit it to render to God that service which is his due. To my certain knowledge, some of the most useful workers in our cause have died through such neglect. To care for the body by providing for it food which is relishable and strengthening, is one of the first duties of the house-holder. Better by far have less expensive clothing and furniture, than to scrimp the supply of necessary articles for the table.

Most people enjoy better health while eating two meals a day than three ; others, under their existing cir-cumstances, may require something to eat at supper-time ; but this meal should be very light. Let no one think himself a criterion for all,— that every one must do ex-actly as he does.

Never cheat the stomach out of that which health de-mands, and never abuse it by placing upon it a load which it should not bear. Cultivate self-control. Restrain ap-petite ; keep it under the control of reason. Do not feel it necessary to load down your table with unhealthful food when you have visitors. The health of your family and the influence upon your children should be considered, as well as the habits and tastes of your guests.

Some health reformers are continually worrying for fear their food, however simple and healthful, will hurt them. To these let me say, Do not think that your food is going to hurt you; but when you have eaten according to your best judgment, and have asked the Lord to bless the food, believe that he has heard your prayer, and be at rest.

Health reform means something to us, and we must not belittle it by narrow views and practices. We must be true to our convictions of right. Daniel was blessed because he was steadfast in doing what he knew to be right, and we shall be blessed if we seek to honor God with full purpose of heart.

HOME EDUCATION.

THE work of the mother is an important one. Amid the homely cares and trying duties of every-day life, she should endeavor to exert an influence that will bless and elevate her household. In the children committed to her care, every mother has a sacred charge from the heavenly Father; and it is her privilege, through the grace of Christ, to mould their character after the divine pattern, to shed an influence over their lives that will draw them toward God and heaven. If mothers had always realized their responsibility, and made it their first purpose, their most important mission, to fit their children for the duties of this life and for the honors of the future, immortal life, we would not see the misery that now exists in so many homes in our land. The mother's work is such that it demands continual advancement in her own life, in order that she may lead her children to higher and still higher attainments. But Satan lays his plans to secure the souls of both parents and children. Mothers are drawn away from the duties of home and the careful training of their little ones, to the service of self and the world. Vanity, fashion, and matters of minor importance are allowed to absorb the attention, and the physical and moral education of the precious children is neglected.

If she makes the customs and practices of the world her criterion, the mother will become unfitted for the responsible duties of her lot. If fashion holds her in bondage, it will weaken her powers of endurance, and make life a wearing burden instead of a blessing. Through physical weakness she may fail to appreciate the value of the opportunities that are hers, and her family may be left to grow up without the benefit of her thought, her prayers, and her diligent instruction. If mothers would only consider the wonderful privileges that God has given them, they would not be so easily turned aside from their sacred duties to the trivial affairs of the world.

The mother's work begins with the babe in her arms. I have often seen the little one throw itself and scream if its will was crossed in any way. This is the time to rebuke the evil spirit. The enemy will try to control the minds of our children, but shall we allow him to mould them according to his will? These little ones cannot discern what spirit is influencing them, and it is the duty of parents to exercise judgment and discretion for them. Their habits must be carefully watched. Evil tendencies are to be restrained, and the mind stimulated in favor of the right. The child should be encouraged in every effort to govern itself.

Regularity should be the rule in all the habits of children. Mothers make a great mistake in permitting them to eat between meals. The stomach becomes deranged by this practice, and the foundation is laid for future suffering. Their fretfulness may have been caused by unwholesome food, still undigested; but the mother feels that she cannot spend time to reason upon the matter, and correct her injurious management. Neither can she stop to soothe their impatient worrying. She gives the little sufferers a piece of cake or some other dainty to quiet them, but this only increases the evil. Some mothers, in their anxiety to do a great amount of work, get wrought up into such nervous haste that they are more irritable than the children, and by scolding and even blows they try to terrify the little ones into quietude.

Mothers often complain of the delicate health of their children, and consult the physician, when, if they would but exercise a little common sense, they would see that the trouble is caused by errors in diet.

We are living in an age of gluttony, and the habits to which the young are educated, even by many Seventh-day Adventists, are in direct opposition to the laws of nature. I was seated once at the table with several children under twelve years of age. Meat was plentifully served, and then a delicate, nervous girl called for pickles. A bottle of chow-chow, fiery with mustard and pungent with spices, was handed her, from which she helped herself freely. The child was proverbial for her nervousness and irritability of temper, and these fiery condiments were well calculated to produce such a condition. The oldest child thought he could not eat a meal without meat, and showed great dissatisfaction, and even disrespect, if it was not provided for him. The mother had indulged him in his likes and dislikes till she had become little better than a slave to his caprices. The lad had not been provided with work, and he spent the greater portion of his time in reading that which was useless or worse than useless. He complained almost constantly of headache, and had no relish for simple food.

Parents should provide employment for their children. Nothing will be a more sure source of evil than indolence. Physical labor that brings healthful weariness to the muscles, will give an appetite for simple, wholesome food, and the youth who is properly employed will not rise from the table grumbling because he does not see before him a platter of meat and various dainties to tempt his appetite.

Jesus, the Son of God, in laboring with his hands at the carpenter's trade, gave an example to all youth. Let those who scorn to take up the common duties of life remember that Jesus was subject to his parents, and contributed his share toward the sustenance of the family. Few luxuries were seen on the table of Joseph and Mary, for they were among the poor and lowly.

Parents should be an example to their children in the expenditure of money. There are those who, as soon as they get money, spend it for dainties to eat, or for needless adornments of dress, and when the supply of money becomes reduced, they feel the need of that which they have wasted. If they have an abundant income, they use every dollar of it; if small, it is not sufficient for the habits of extravagance they have acquired, and they borrow to supply the demand. They gather from any source possible to meet their fancied necessities. They become dishonest and untruthful, and the record that stands against them in the books of heaven is such as they will not care to look upon in the day of Judgment. The desire of the eye must be gratified, the craving of the appetite indulged, and they keep themselves poor by their improvident habits, when they might have learned to live within their means. Extravagance is one of the sins to which youth are prone. They despise economical habits, for fear they shall be thought niggardly and mean. What will Jesus, the Majesty of heaven, who has given them an example of patient industry and economy, say to such?

It is not necessary to specify here how economy may be practiced in every particular. Those whose hearts are fully surrendered to God, and who take his word as their guide, will know how to conduct themselves in all the duties of life. They will learn of Jesus, who is meek and lowly of heart; and in cultivating the meekness of Christ they will close the door against innumerable temptations.

They will not be studying how to gratify appetite and the passion for display, while so many cannot even keep hunger from the door. The amount daily spent in needless things, with the thought, "It is only a nickle," "It is only a dime," seems very little; but multiply these littles by the days of the year, and as the years go by, the array of figures will seem almost incredible.

The Lord has been pleased to present before me the evils which result from spendthrift habits, that I might admonish parents to teach their children strict economy. Teach them that money spent for that which they do not need, is perverted from its proper use. He that is unfaithful in that which is least, would be unfaithful in much. If men are unfaithful with earthly goods, they cannot be intrusted with the eternal riches. Set a guard over the appetite; teach your children by example as well as by precept to use a simple diet. Teach them to be industrious, not merely busy, but engaged in useful labor. Seek to arouse the moral sensibilities. Teach them that

God has claims upon them, even from the early years of their childhood. Tell them that there are moral corruptions to be met on every hand, that they need to come to Jesus and give themselves to him, body and spirit, and that in him they will find strength to resist every temptation. Keep before their minds that they were not created merely to please themselves, but to be the Lord's agent for noble purposes. Teach them, when temptations urge into paths of selfish indulgence, when Satan is seeking to shut out God from their sight, to look to Jesus, pleading, "Save, Lord, that I be not overcome." Angels will gather about them in answer to their prayer, and lead them into safe paths.

Christ prayed for his disciples, not that they should be taken out of the world, but that they should be kept from evil,— that they might be kept from yielding to the temptations they would meet on every hand. This is a prayer that should be offered up by every father and mother. But should they thus plead with God in behalf of their children, and then leave them to do as they please? Should they pamper the appetite until it gets the mastery, and then expect to restrain the children? — No; temperance and self-control should be taught from the very cradle up. Upon the mother must rest largely the responsibility of this work. The tenderest earthly tie is that between the mother and her child. The child is more readily impressed by the life and example of the mother than by that of the father, because of this stronger and more tender bond of union. Yet the mother's responsibility is a heavy one, and should have the constant aid of the father.

Intemperance in eating and drinking, intemperance in labor, intemperance in almost everything, exists on every hand. Those who make great exertions to accomplish just so much work in a given time, and continue to labor when their judgment tells them they should rest, are never gainers. They are living on borrowed capital. They are expending the vital force which they will need at a future time. And when the energy they have so recklessly used is demanded, they fail for want of it. The physical strength is gone, the mental powers fail. They realize that they have met with a loss, but do not know what it is. Their time of need has come, but their physical resources are exhausted. Every one who violates the laws of health must sometime be a sufferer to a greater or less degree. God has provided us with constitutional force, which will be needed at different periods of our life. If we recklessly exhaust this force by continual overtaxation, we shall sometime be losers. Our usefulness will be lessened, if not our life itself destroyed.

As a rule, the labor of the day should not be prolonged into the evening. If all the hours of the day are well improved, the work extended into the evening is so much extra, and the overtaxed system will suffer from the burden imposed upon it. I have been shown that those who do this, often lose much more than they gain, for their energies are exhausted, and they labor on nervous excitement. They may not realize any immediate injury, but they are surely undermining their constitution.

Let parents devote the evenings to their families. Lay off care and perplexity with the labors of the day. The husband and father would gain much if he would make it a rule not to mar the happiness of his family by bringing his business troubles home to fret and worry over. He may need the council of his wife in difficult matters, and they may both obtain relief in their perplexities by unitedly seeking wisdom of God; but to keep the mind constantly strained upon business affairs will injure the health of both mind and body.

Let the evenings be spent as happily as possible. Let home be a place where cheerfulness, courtesy, and love exist. This will make it attractive to the children. If the parents are continually borrowing trouble, are irritable and fault-finding, the children partake of the same spirit of dissatisfaction and contention, and home is the most miserable place in the world. The children find more pleasure among strangers, in reckless company, or in the street, than at home. All this might be avoided if temperance in all things were practiced, and patience cultivated. Self-control on the part of all the members of the family will make home almost a paradise. Make your rooms as cheerful as possible. Let the children find home the most attractive place on earth. Throw about them such influences that they will not seek for street companions, nor think of the haunts of vice except with horror. If the home-life is what it should be, the habits formed there will be a strong defense against the assaults of temptation when the young shall leave the shelter of home for the world.

Do we build our houses for the happiness of the family, or merely for display? Do we provide pleasant, sunny rooms for our children, or do we keep them darkened and closed, reserving them for strangers who are not dependent on us for happiness? There is no nobler work that we can do, no greater benefit that we can confer upon society, than to give to our children a proper education impressing upon them, by precept and example, the important principle that purity of life and sincerity of purpose will best qualify them to act their part in the world.

Our artificial habits deprive us of many privileges and much enjoyment, and unfit us for usefulness. A fashionable life is a hard, thankless life. How often time, money, and health are sacrificed, the patience sorely tried, and self-control lost, merely for the sake of display. If parents would cling to simplicity, not indulging in expense for the gratification of vanity, and to follow fashion; if they would maintain a noble independence in the right, unmoved by the influence of those, who, while professing Christ, refuse to lift the cross of self-denial, they would by their example itself give their children an invaluable education. The children would become men and women of moral worth, and, in their turn, would have courage to stand bravely for the right, even against the current of fashion and popular opinion.

Every act of the parents tells on the future of the children. In devoting time and money to the outward adorning and the gratification of perverted appetite, they are cultivating vanity, selfishness, and lust in the children. Mothers complain of being so burdened with care and labor that they cannot take time patiently to instruct their little ones, and to sympathize with them in their disappointments and trials. Young hearts yearn for sympathy and tenderness, and if they do not obtain it from their parents, they will seek it from sources that may endanger both mind and morals. I have heard mothers refuse their children some innocent pleasure, for lack of time and thought, while their busy fingers and weary eyes were diligently engaged on some useless piece of adorning, something which could only serve to encourage vanity and extravagance in the children. "As the twig is bent, the tree is inclined." As the children approach manhood and womanhood, these lessons bear fruit in pride and moral worthlessness. The parents deplore the children's faults, but are blind to the fact that they are but reaping the crop from seed of their own planting.

Christian parents, take up your life burden, and think candidly of the sacred obligations that rest upon you. Make the word of God your standard, instead of following the fashions and customs of the world, the lust of the eye, and the pride of life. The future happiness of your families and the welfare of society depend largely upon the physical and moral education which your children receive in the first years of their life. If their tastes and habits are as simple in all things as they should be, if the dress is tidy, without extra adornment, mothers will find time to make their children happy, and teach them loving obedience.

Do not send your little ones away to school too early. The mother should be careful how she trusts the moulding of the infant mind to other hands. Parents ought to be the best teachers of their children till they have reached eight or ten years of age. Their school-room should be the open air, amid the flowers and birds, and their text-book the treasures of nature. As fast as their minds can comprehend it, the parents should open before them God's great book of nature. These lessons, given amid such surroundings, will not soon be forgotten. Great pains should be taken to prepare the soil of the heart for the "Sower" to scatter the good seed. If half the time and labor that is now worse than wasted in following the fashions of the world, were devoted to the cultivation of the minds of the children, to the formation of correct habits, a marked change would be apparent in families.

Not long since I heard a mother say that she liked to see a house fitly constructed, that defects in the arrangement and mismatched wood-work in the finishing annoyed her. I do not condemn nice taste in this respect, but as I listened to her, I regretted that this nicety could not have been brought into her methods of managing her children. These were buildings for whose framing she was responsible; yet their rough, uncourteous ways, their passionate, selfish natures and uncontrolled wills, were painfully apparent to others. Ill-formed characters, mismatched pieces of humanity, indeed they were, yet the mother was blind to it all. The arrangement of her house was of more consequence to her than the symmetry of her children's character.

Cleanliness and order are Christian duties, yet even these may be carried too far, and made the one essential, while matters of greater importance are neglected. Those who neglect the interests of the children for these considerations, are tithing the mint and cummin, while they neglect the weightier matters of the law,—justice, mercy, and the love of God.

Those children who are the most indulged become willful, passionate, and unlovely. Would that parents could realize that upon judicious early training depends the happiness of both the parents and the children. Who are these little ones that are committed to our care?

They are the younger members of the Lord's family.

"Take this son, this daughter," he says, "nurse them for me, and fit them up 'that they may be polished after the similitude of a palace,' that they may shine in the courts of the Lord." Precious work! important work! Yet we see mothers sighing for a wider field of labor, for some missionary work to do. If they could only go to Africa or India, they would feel that they were doing something. But to take up the little daily duties of life, and carry them forward faithfully, perseveringly, seems to them an unimportant thing. Why is this? Is it not often because the mother's work is so rarely appreciated? She has a thousand cares and burdens of which the father seldom has any knowledge. Too often he returns home bringing with him his cares and business perplexities to over-shadow the family, and if he does not find everything just to his mind at home, he gives expression to his feelings in impatience and fault-finding. He can boast of what he has achieved through the day; but the mother's work, to his mind, amounts to little, or at least is undervalued. To him her cares appear trifling. She has only to cook the meals, look after the children, sometimes a large family of them, and keep the house in order. She has tried all day to keep the domestic machinery running smoothly. She has tried, though tired and perplexed, to speak kindly and cheerfully, and to instruct the children and keep them in the right path. All this has cost effort, and much patience on her part. She cannot, in her turn, boast of what she has done. It seems to her as though she has accomplished nothing. But it is not so. Though the results of her work are not apparent, angels of God are watching the careworn mother, noting the burdens she carries from day to day. Her name may never appear upon the records of history, or receive the honor and applause of the world, as may that of the husband and father; but it is immortalized in the book of God. She is doing what she can, and her position in God's sight is more exalted than that of a king upon his throne; for she is dealing with character, she is fashioning minds.

The mothers of the present day are making the society of the future. How important that their children be so brought up that they shall be able to resist the temptations they will meet on every side in later life!

Whatever may be his calling and its perplexities, let the father take into his home the same smiling countenance and pleasant tones with which he has all day greeted visitors and strangers. Let the wife feel that she can lean upon the large affections of her husband,—that his arms will strengthen and uphold her through all her toils and cares, that his influence will sustain hers, and her burden will lose half its weight. Are the children not his as well as hers?

Let the father seek to lighten the mother's task. In the time that he would devote to selfish enjoyment of leisure, let him seek to become acquainted with his children — associate with them in their sports, in their work. Let him point them to the beautiful flowers, the lofty trees, in whose very leaves they can trace the work and love of God. He should teach them that the God who made all these things loves the beautiful and the good. Christ pointed his disciples to the lilies of the field and the birds of the air, showing how God cares for them, and presenting this as evidence that he will care for man, who is of higher consequence than birds or flowers. Tell the children that however much time may be wasted in attempts at display, our appearance can never compare, for grace and beauty, with that of the simplest flowers of the field. Thus their minds may be drawn from the artificial to the natural. They may learn that God has given them all these beautiful things to enjoy, and that he wants them to give him the heart's best and holiest affections.

Parents should seek to awaken in their children an interest in the study of physiology. Youth need to be instructed in regard to their own bodies. There are but few among the young who have any definite knowledge of the mysteries of life. The study of the wonderful human organism, the relation and dependence of all its complicated parts, is one in which most mothers take little if any interest. They do not understand the influence of the body upon the mind, or of the mind upon the body. They occupy themselves with needless trifles, and then plead that they have no time to obtain the information which they need in order to care properly for the health of their children. It is less trouble to trust them to the doctors. Thousands of children die through ignorance of the laws of their being.

If parents themselves would obtain knowledge upon this subject, and feel the importance of putting it to a practical use, we should see a better condition of things. Teach your children to reason from cause to effect. Show them that if they violate the laws of their being, they must pay the penalty by suffering. If you cannot see as rapid improvement as you desire, do not be discouraged, but instruct them patiently, and press on until victory is gained. Continue to teach them in regard to their own bodies, and how to take care of them. Recklessness in regard to bodily health tends to recklessness in morals.

Do not neglect to teach your children how to prepare healthful food. In giving them these lessons in physiology and in good cooking, you are giving them the first steps in some of the most useful branches of education, and inculcating principles which are needful elements in a religious education.

All the lessons of which I have spoken in this article are needed. If properly heeded, they will be like a bulwark that will preserve our children from the evils which are flooding the world. We want temperance at our tables. We want houses where the God-given sunlight and the pure air of heaven are welcomed. We want a cheerful, happy influence in our homes. We must cultivate useful habits in our children, and must instruct them in the things of God. It costs something to do all this. It costs prayers and tears, and patient, oft-repeated instruction. We are sometimes put to our wit's end to know what to do ; but we can take the children to God in our prayers, pleading that they may be kept from evil, praying, " Now, Lord, do thy work; soften and subdue the hearts of our children." And he will hear us. He hearkens to the prayers of the weeping, careworn mothers. When Christ was on earth, the burdened mothers brought their children to him ; they thought that if he would lay his hands upon them, they would have better courage to bring them up as they ought to go. The Saviour knew why these mothers came to him with their little ones, and he rebuked the disciples, who would have kept them away, saying, "Suffer the little children to come unto me, and forbid them not; for of such is the kingdom of God." * Jesus loves the little ones, and he is watching to see how parents are doing their work.

Iniquity abounds on every hand, and if the children are saved, earnest, persevering effort must be put forth. Christ has said, "I sanctify myself, that they also might be sanctified." † He wanted his disciples to be sanctified, and he made himself their example, that they might follow him. What if fathers and mothers should take this same position, saying, " I want my children to have steadfast principles, and I will give them an example of this in my life" ? Let the mother think no sacrifice too great, if made for the salvation of her household. Remember, Jesus gave his life for the purpose of rescuing you and yours from ruin. You will have his sympathy and help in this blessed work, and will be a laborer together with God.

In whatever else we may fail, let us be thorough in the work for our children. If they go forth from the home-training pure and virtuous, if they fill the least and lowest place in God's great plan of good for the world, our life-work can never be called a failure.

* Mark 10:14.   † John 17:19.

OVERBURDENED HOUSEKEEPERS.

WITH many, the all-absorbing object of life,— that which justifies any expenditure or labor, — is to appear in the latest style. Education, health, and comfort are sacrificed at the shrine of fashion. Even in the table arrangements, fashion and show exert their baleful influence. The healthful preparation of food becomes a secondary matter. The serving of a great variety of dishes absorbs time, money, and taxing labor, without accomplishing any good. It may be fashionable to have half a dozen courses at a meal, but the custom is ruinous to health. It is a fashion that sensible men and women should condemn, by both precept and example. Do have a little regard for the life of your cook. "Is not the life more than meat, and the body than raiment?"*

In these days, domestic duties claim almost the whole time of the housekeeper. How much better it would be for the health of the household, if the table preparations were more simple. Thousands of lives are sacrificed every year at this altar,— lives which might have been prolonged had it not been for this endless of manufactured duties. Many a mother goes down to the grave, who, had her habits been simple, might have lived to be a blessing in the home, the church, and the world.

Satan is the inventor of these customs with which the society of our day is overburdened, and many of the votaries of fashion know no better way than to spend their precious probationary time in the almost fruitless endeavor to keep up with her ever-changing decrees. What account can they render in the Judgment to God, who has a just claim upon their time, their strength, and all their powers?

There is a general cry all over our land, "Where shall I find a good housekeeper, one who knows how to cook?" Indeed, the dearth of good cooks and housekeepers is

* Matt. 6: 25. (73)

becoming alarming. If this state of things continues, we shall be left entirely destitute of good domestic help.

But what is the reason for this fear of household duties among our girls? The great reason is, that such labor has been considered a disgrace. As a general thing, the cook has not received the respect due her. I have seen people, once poor but now rich, whose good sense seemed to have fled with their poverty, and they became superficial in everything. Some who learn to be seamstresses, type-setters, proof-readers, book-keepers, or school-teachers, consider themselves too aristocratic to associate with the cook.

These ideas have pervaded nearly all classes of society. The cook is made to feel that her occupation is one which places her low in the scale of social life, and that she must not expect to associate with the family on equal terms. Can you be surprised, then, that intelligent girls seek some other employment? Do you marvel that there are so few educated cooks? The only marvel is that there are so many who will submit to such treatment.

The cook fills an important place in the household. She is preparing food to be taken into the stomach, to form brain, bone, and muscle. The health of all the members of the family depends largely upon her skill and intelligence. Household duties will never receive the attention they demand until those who faithfully perform them are held in proper respect.

Self-love, self-worship, idolatry of self, have bound upon the necks of women a yoke grievous to be borne. They are weighed down with burdens heavy to carry. And this wearisome labor in the interest of fashion is repaid only by suffering and oppression. Christ, looking down the ages, saw the state of things which now exists, and to these overladen ones he gives the blessed invitation, "Come unto me, all ye that labor and are heavy laden, and I will give you rest. Take my yoke upon you, and learn of me; for I am meek and lowly in heart, and ye shall find rest unto your souls." *

* Matt. 11 : 28, 29.

PARENTAL RESPONSIBILITY.

GOD has permitted the light of health reform to shine upon us in these last days, that by walking in the light we may escape many of the dangers to which we shall be exposed. Satan is working with great power to lead men to indulge appetite, gratify inclination, and spend their days in heedless folly. He presents attractions in a life of selfish enjoyment and of sensual indulgence. Intemperance saps the energies of both mind and body. He who is thus overcome has placed himself upon Satan's ground, where he will be tempted and annoyed, and finally controlled at pleasure by the enemy of all righteousness.

Parents need to be impressed with their obligation to give to the world children having well-developed character,— children who will have moral power to resist temptation, and whose life will be an honor to God and a blessing to their fellow-men. Those who enter upon active life with firm principles, will be prepared to stand unsullied amid the moral pollutions of this corrupt age. Let mothers improve every opportunity to educate their children for usefulness.

The work of the mother is sacred and important. She should teach her children, from the cradle up, habits of self-denial and self-control. Her time, in a special sense, belongs to her children. But if it is mostly occupied with the follies of this degenerate age, if society, dress, and amusements absorb her attention, her children will fail to be suitably educated.

Many mothers who deplore the intemperance that exists everywhere, do not look deep enough to see the cause. Too often it may be traced to the home table. Many a mother, even among those who profess to be Christians, is daily setting before her household rich and highly seasoned food, which tempts the appetite and encourages overeating. In some families, flesh-meats constitute the principal article of diet, and in consequence, the blood is filled with cancerous and scrofulous humors. Then when suffering and disease follow, Providence is charged with that which is the result of a wrong course. I repeat: intemperance begins at the table, and, with the majority, appetite is indulged until indulgence becomes second nature.

Whoever eats too much, or of food which is not healthful, is weakening his power to resist the clamors of other appetites and passions. Many parents, to avoid the task of patiently educating their children to habits of self-denial, indulge them in eating and drinking whenever they please. The desire to satisfy the taste and to gratify inclination does not lessen with the increase of years; and these indulged youth, as they grow up, are governed by impulse, slaves to appetite. When they take their place in society, and begin life for themselves, they are powerless to resist temptation. In the glutton, the tobacco-devotee, the wine-bibber, and the inebriate, we see the evil results of erroneous education and of self-indulgence.

When we hear the sad lamentation of Christian men and women over the terrible evils of intemperance, the questions at once arise: Who have educated the youth? who have fostered in them these unruly appetites? who have neglected the solemn responsibility of forming their character for usefulness in this life, and for the society of heavenly angels in the next?

When parents and children meet at the final reckoning, what a scene will be presented! Thousands of children who have been slaves to appetite and debasing vice, whose lives are moral wrecks, will stand face to face with the parents who made them what they are. Who but the parents must bear this fearful responsibility? Did the Lord make these youth corrupt?—Oh, no! Who, then, has done this fearful work? Were not the sins of the parents transmitted to the children in perverted appetites and passions? and was not the work completed by those who neglected to train them according to the pattern which God has given? Just as surely as they exist, all these parents will pass in review before God.

Satan is ready to do his work; he will not neglect to present allurements which the children have no will or moral power to resist. I saw that, through his temptations, he is instituting ever-changing fashions, and attractive parties and amusements, that mothers may be led to devote their time to frivolous matters, instead of to the education and training of their children. Our youth need mothers who will teach them from the cradle to control passion, to deny appetite, and to overcome selfishness. They need line upon line, precept upon precept, here a little and there a little.

The Hebrews were taught how to train their children so that they might avoid the idolatry and wickedness of the heathen nations: "Therefore shall ye lay up these my words in your heart and in your soul, and bind them for a sign upon your hand, that they may be as frontlets between your eyes. And ye shall teach them your children, speaking of them when thou sittest in thine house, and when thou walkest by the way, when thou liest down, and when thou risest up." *

Woman should fill the position which God originally designed for her, as her husband's equal. The world needs mothers who are mothers not merely in name, but in every sense of the word. We may safely say that the distinctive duties of woman are more sacred, more holy, than those of man. Let woman realize the sacredness of her work, and in the strength and fear of God take up her life mission. Let her educate her children for usefulness in this world, and for a home in the better world.

The position of a woman in her family is more sacred than that of the king upon his throne. Her great work is to make her life an example such as she would wish her children to copy. And by precept as well as example, she is to store their minds with useful knowledge, and lead them to self-sacrificing labor for the good of others. The

* Deut. 11 : 18, 19.

great stimulus to the toiling, burdened mother should be that every child who is trained aright, and who has the inward adorning, the ornament of a meek and quiet spirit, will shine in the courts of the Lord.

I entreat Christian mothers to realize their responsibility, and to live, not to please themselves, but to glorify God. Christ pleased not himself, but took upon him the form of a servant. He left the royal courts, and clothed his divinity with humanity, that by his own example he might teach us how we may be exalted to the position of sons and daughters in the royal family, children of the heavenly King. But what are the conditions upon which we may obtain this great blessing?—"Come out from among them, and be ye separate, saith the Lord, and touch not the unclean; and I will receive you, and will be a father unto you, and ye shall be my sons and daughters." *

Christ humbled himself from the position of one equal with God to that of a servant. His home was in Nazareth, a place proverbial for its wickedness. His parents were among the lowly poor. His trade was that of a carpenter, and he labored with his hands to do his part in sustaining the family. For thirty years he was subject to his parents. The life of Christ points out our duty to be diligent in labor, and to provide for those intrusted to our care.

In his lessons of instruction to his disciples, Jesus taught them that his kingdom is not a worldly kingdom, where all are striving for the highest position; but he gave them lessons in humility and self-sacrifice for the good of others. His humility did not consist in a low estimate of his own character and qualifications, but in adapting himself to fallen humanity, in order to raise them up with him to a higher life. Yet how few see anything attractive in the humility of Christ! Worldlings are constantly striving to exalt themselves one above another; but Jesus, the Son of God, humbled himself in order to uplift man. The true disciple of Christ will follow his example.

* 2 Cor. 6 : 17, 18.

Would that the mothers of this generation might feel the sacredness of their mission, not trying to vie with their wealthy neighbors in appearance, but seeking to honor God by the faithful performance of duty. If right principles in regard to temperance were implanted in the youth who are to form and mould society, there would be little necessity for temperance crusades. Firmness of character, moral control, would prevail, and in the strength of Jesus the temptations of these last days would be resisted.

It is a most difficult matter to unlearn the habits which have been indulged through life. The demon of intemperance is of giant strength, and is not easily conquered. But let parents begin the crusade against it at their own firesides, in their own families, in the principles they teach their children from their very infancy, and then they may hope for success. It will pay you, mothers, to use the precious hours which are given you by God in forming the character of your children, and in teaching them to adhere strictly to the principles of temperance in eating and drinking.

A sacred trust is committed to parents, to guard the physical and moral constitution of their children, so that the nervous system may be well balanced, and the soul not endangered. Fathers and mothers should understand the laws of life, that they may not, through ignorance, allow wrong tendencies to develop in their children. The diet affects both physical and moral health. How carefully, then, should mothers study to supply the table with the most simple, healthful food, in order that the digestive organs may not be weakened, the nerves unbalanced, or the instruction which they give their children counteracted.

Satan sees that he cannot have so great power over minds when the appetite is kept under control as when it is indulged, and he is constantly working to lead men to indulgence. Under the influence of unhealthful food, the conscience becomes stupefied, the mind is darkened, and its susceptibility to impressions is impaired. But the guilt of the transgressor is not lessened because the conscience has been violated till it has become insensible.

Since a healthy state of mind depends upon the normal condition of the vital forces, what care should be exercised that neither stimulants nor narcotics be used! Yet we see that a large number of those who profess to be Christians are using tobacco. They deplore the evils of intemperance; yet while speaking against the use of liquors, these very men will eject the juice of tobacco. There must be a change of sentiment with reference to tobacco-using before the root of the evil will be reached. We press the subject still closer. Tea and coffee are fostering the appetite for stronger stimulants. And then we come still closer home, to the preparation of food, and ask, Is temperance practiced in all things? are the reforms which are essential to health and happiness carried out here?

Every true Christian will have control of his appetites and passions. Unless he is free from the bondage of appetite, he cannot be a true, obedient servant of Christ. The indulgence of appetite and passion blunts the effect of truth upon the heart. It is impossible for the spirit and power of the truth to sanctify a man, soul, body, and spirit, when he is controlled by sensual desires.

EDUCATION AND HEALTH.

FOR generations the prevailing system of education has been destructive to health, and even to life itself. Many parents and teachers fail to understand that in the child's early years the greatest attention needs to be given to the physical constitution, that a healthy condition of body and brain may be secured. It has been the custom to encourage sending children to school when they were mere babies, needing a mother's care. In many instances the little ones are crowded into ill-ventilated school-rooms, where they sit in improper positions, upon poorly constructed benches, and as the result the young and tender frames often become deformed. Little children, whose limbs and muscles are not strong, and whose brains are undeveloped, are kept confined, to their injury. Many have but a slight hold on life to begin with, and confinement in school from day to day makes them nervous, and they become diseased. Their bodies are dwarfed in consequence of the exhausted condition of the nervous system. Yet when the lamp of life goes out, parents and teachers do not realize that they were in any way responsible for quenching the vital spark. Standing by the grave of their child, the afflicted parents look upon their bereavement as a special dispensation of Providence, when it was their own inexcusably ignorant course that destroyed the young life. Under such circumstances, to charge the death to Providence savors of blasphemy. God wants the little ones to live, and receive a right education, that they may develop a beautiful character, glorify him in this world, and praise him in the better world.

Parents and teachers take the responsibility of training these children, yet how few of them realize their duty before God to become acquainted with the physical organism, that they may know how to preserve the life and health of those who are placed in their charge. Thousands of children die because of the ignorance of those who care for them.

Many children have been ruined for life, and some have died, as the result of the injudicious course of parents and teachers, in forcing the young intellect while neglecting the physical nature. The children were too young to be in a school-room. Their minds were taxed with lessons when they should have been left untasked until the physical strength was sufficient to support mental effort. Small children should be as free as lambs to run out-of-doors. They should be allowed the most favorable opportunity to lay the foundation for a sound constitution.

Youth who are kept in school, and confined to close study, cannot have sound health. Mental effort without corresponding physical exercise, calls an undue proportion of blood to the brain, and thus the circulation is unbalanced. The brain has too much blood, while the extremities have too little. The hours of study and recreation should be carefully regulated, and a portion of the time should be spent in physical labor. When the habits of students in eating and drinking, dressing and sleeping, are in accordance with physical law, they can obtain an education without sacrificing health. The lesson must be often repeated, and pressed home to the conscience, that education will be of little value if there is no physical strength to use it after it is gained.

Students should not be permitted to take so many studies that they will have no time for physical training. The health cannot be preserved unless some portion of each day is given to muscular exertion in the open air. Stated hours should be devoted to manual labor of some kind, anything which will call into action all parts of the body. Equalize the taxation of the mental and the physical powers, and the mind of the student will be refreshed.

If he is diseased, physical exercise will often help the system to recover its normal condition. When students leave college, they should have better health and a better understanding of the laws of life than when they entered it. The health should be as sacredly guarded as the character.

Many students are deplorably ignorant of the fact that diet exerts a powerful influence upon the health. Some have never made a determined effort to control the appetite, or to observe proper rules in regard to diet. They eat too much, even at their meals, and some eat between meals whenever the temptation is presented. If those who profess to be Christians desire to solve the questions so perplexing to them, why their minds are so dull, why their religious aspirations are so feeble, they need not, in many instances, go farther than the table ; here is cause enough, if there were no other.

Many separate themselves from God by their indulgence of appetite. He who notices the fall of a sparrow, who numbers the very hairs of the head, marks the sin of those who indulge perverted appetite at the expense of weakening the physical powers, benumbing the intellect, and deadening the moral perceptions.

The teachers themselves should give proper attention to the laws of health, that they may preserve their own powers in the best possible condition, and by example as well as by precept may exert a right influence upon their pupils. The teacher whose physical powers are already enfeebled by disease or overwork, should pay especial attention to the laws of life. He should take time for recreation. He should not take upon himself responsibilities outside of his school-work, which will so tax him, physically or mentally, that his nervous system will be unbalanced ; for in this case he will be unfitted to deal with minds, and cannot do justice to himself or to his pupils.

Our institutions of learning should be provided with

every facility for instruction regarding the mechanism of the human system. Students should be taught how to breathe, how to read and speak so that the strain will not come on the throat and lungs, but on the abdominal muscles. Teachers need to educate themselves in this direction. Our students should have a thorough training, that they may enter upon active life with an intelligent knowledge of the habitation which God has given them. Teach them that they must be learners as long as they live. And while you are teaching them, remember that they will teach others. Your lessons will be repeated for the benefit of many more than sit before you day by day.

DRESS.

FASHION rules the world; and she is a tyrannical mistress, often compelling her devotees to submit to the greatest inconvenience and discomfort. Fashion taxes without reason, and collects without mercy. She has a fascinating power, and stands ready to criticise and ridicule all who do not follow in her wake.

Satan, the instigator and prime mover in the ever-changing, never-satisfying decrees of fashion, is always busy devising something new that shall prove an injury to physical and moral health; and he triumphs that his devices succeed so well. Death laughs that the health-destroying folly and blind zeal of the worshipers at fashion's shrine bring them so easily under his dominion. Happiness and the favor of God are laid upon her altar.

We see the world absorbed in vain amusements. The first and best thoughts of the larger portion are given to dress, and the culture of mind and heart is neglected. Even among those who profess to love and keep the commandments of God, there are some who ape this class as nearly as they possibly can and retain the name of Christian. Some of the young are so eager for display that they are willing to give up even the Christian name if they can only indulge their vanity in dress.

On Sunday many of the popular churches appear more like a theater than like a place for the worship of God. Every style of fashionable dress is displayed there. Many of the poor have not courage to enter such houses of worship. Their plain dress, though it may be neat, is in marked contrast with that of their more wealthy sisters, and this difference causes them to feel embarrassed. Some try to appear like the wealthy by trimming goods of an inferior quality in imitation of more costly apparel. Poor girls, receiving but small wages, often spend their

last cent in order to dress like those who are not obliged
to earn their own living. In consequence, they have nothing laid by for sickness, nothing to put into the treasury
of God, no time to improve the mind or to study God's
word, no time for secret prayer or the prayer-meeting.

It is a lamentable fact that many professed Christian
women take the lead in patronizing the fashions ; and those
who make no pretensions to religion, follow in their steps.
Some who are in humble circumstances, in their efforts to
keep pace with the ever-changing styles of dress, endure
privation, and work far beyond their strength, in order to
retain their place in fashionable society. This temptation
is so strong that some, in trying to gain their object,
are guilty of dishonesty and theft. Many are led to ruin
by the desire for self-adornment. Professed Christians who
have, by their example, opened a door of temptation to
their weak sisters, will have a fearful account to meet in
the day of final reckoning. Inexperienced ones, charmed
with the respect paid to those who dress stylishly, become
so infatuated that nothing is too precious to exchange for
artificial decorations.

While superfluous trimming and ornaments are to be
avoided, as opposed to our profession as followers of the
meek and lowly Jesus, we would not discourage the exercise of correct taste, neatness, and order in dress. There
are those who are careless of their apparel, and are always harping on pride in dress. They think it a virtue
to be untidy, and to dress without order or taste. They
class decency and neatness with pride, and excuse themselves for their neglect of apparel, even upon the Sabbath, under pretense of carrying out that separation from
the world which the word of God requires of his people.
If these persons had an engagement to meet a friend
honored by the world, and they wished to be especially
favored by him, they would exert themselves to appear
in his presence with the best and neatest apparel they
could obtain. Yet when they meet upon the Sabbath to
worship the great God, they think it is of no consequence

in what dress they appear, or what is the condition of their person. In His house, which is as the audience-chamber of the Most High, where heavenly angels are in attendance, they assemble with but little respect or reverence. All who meet upon the Sabbath to worship God, should, if possible, have neat, well-fitting, comely garments to wear in the house of worship. It is a dishonor to the Sabbath, to God, and to his house, for those who profess to believe that the Sabbath is the holy of the Lord, and honorable, to wear upon that day the soiled clothing which they have worn through the labors of the week, if they can obtain anything more suitable.

The followers of Christ are represented by him as the salt of the earth and the light of the world. Without the saving influence of Christians, the world would perish in its own corruption. Look upon the class of professed Christians described, who are careless of their dress and person, and loose in business transactions. Think you if our Saviour were upon earth he would point to them as the salt of the earth and the light of the world?—No, never. True Christians are elevated in their conversation; and while they believe it to be a sin to condescend to foolish flattery, they are courteous, kind, and benevolent. Their words are those of sincerity and truth. They are faithful in their dealings with their brethren and with the world. In their dress they avoid superfluity and display; but their clothing is modest, and arranged upon the person with order and taste. They are more anxious for their bodies to be in a condition to glorify God, than they are to be clothed according to the latest dictates of fashion.

The suffering caused among women by unhealthful dress cannot be estimated. Many have become life-long invalids through their compliance with the demands of fashion. Health and life have been sacrificed to the insatiable goddess. Many seem to think they have a right to treat their bodies as they please; but they forget that their bodies are not their own. The Creator who formed them has claims upon them that they cannot lightly throw off. Every needless transgression of the laws of our be-ing is virtually a transgression of the law of God, and is sin in the sight of Heaven. The Creator knew how to form the human body. He did not need to consult the mantua-makers in regard to their ideas of beauty. God, who created everything that is lovely and glorious in nature, understood how to make the human form beauti-ful and healthy. The modern improvements upon his plan are insulting to the Creator. They deform that which he made perfect.

It is Satan's design so to pervert every function of our being that life may be made miserable, and God may be dishonored in the creatures he has made. If women make the customs of the world their criterion, they will become unfitted, both physically and mentally, for the duties of life. Many have done themselves untold injury by compressing the waist. Their power to do good in the family and in society is greatly lessened; and if they are mothers, their children are robbed of vitality. When the waist is compressed, the circulation of the blood is impeded, and the internal organs, cramped and crowded out of place, cannot perform their work properly. It is impossible, under such circumstances, to take a full in-spiration. Thus the pernicious habit of breathing only with the upper part of the lungs is formed, and feeble-ness and disease are often the result.

The dangers resulting from compression of the waist are not realized by the majority of women, though many able pens have treated upon the subject. Many claim that tight-lacing is now nearly or quite abandoned, and such may think these remarks are uncalled-for; but it is true to-day that the clothing of most women is worn too tight for the proper action of the vital organs. Every article of dress upon the person should be worn so loose that in raising the arms the clothing will be correspondingly lifted.

Another error in the dress of women of the present

day is that of wearing their skirts so that the weight is sustained by the hips alone. This heavy weight, pressing upon the bowels, drags them downward, and causes weakness of the stomach and a feeling of lassitude, which leads the sufferer to incline forward. This tends further to cramp the lungs, and prevent their proper action. The blood becomes impure, the pores of the skin fail in their office, sallowness and disease result, and beauty and health are gone. Ladies may resort to cosmetics to restore the tint of the complexion, but they cannot thus bring back the glow of health. That which renders the skin dark and dingy, also clouds the spirits, and destroys cheerfulness and peace of mind. Every woman who values health should avoid hanging any weight upon the hips. The shoulders should sustain the weight of every article of clothing worn upon the person. This will go far to prevent the weaknesses which prevail among women to such an alarming extent.

The limbs, which should have even more covering than any other portion of the body, because farthest from the center of circulation, are often not suitably protected; while over the vital organs, where there is naturally more warmth than in other portions of the body, there is an undue proportion of covering. The heavy draperies often worn upon the back, induce heat and congestion in the sensitive organs which lie beneath. This fashionable attire is one of the greatest causes of disease among women. Perfect health depends upon perfect circulation. If the limbs are properly clothed, fewer skirts are needed. These should not be so heavy as to impede the motion of the limbs, nor so long as to gather the dampness and filth of the ground, and their weight should be suspended from the shoulders. The dress should fit easily, obstructing neither the circulation of the blood, nor a free, full, natural respiration. The feet should be suitably protected from cold and damp. Clad in this way, we can take exercise in the open air, even in the dew of morning or evening, or after a fall of snow or rain, without fear of taking cold. Exercise in the invigorating air of heaven is necessary to a healthy circulation of the blood. It is the best safeguard against colds, coughs, and the internal congestions which lay the foundation of so many diseases. True dress reform regulates every article of clothing. If those ladies who are failing in health would lay off their fashionable robes, clothe themselves suitably for out-door enjoyment, and exercise in the open air, carefully at first, increasing the amount as they can endure it, many of them might recover health, and live to bless the world with their example and the work of their hands.

It is not the will of God that men and women should die prematurely, leaving their work unfinished. He would have us live out the full measure of our days, with every organ free to do its allotted work. Many complain of the providences of God when disease and death remove members of the household; but it is unjust to charge God with what is but the sure result of their own transgression of natural laws.

Fashionable mothers clothe their little girls as unhealthfully as they do themselves. Their waists are compressed at an early age, and the limbs are left with but slight protection, when the forces of nature need every advantage to enable them to perfect the physical frame. The limbs were not formed to endure exposure, as was the face. Children who are clothed according to fashion cannot be out-doors much, unless the weather is mild. Therefore they are kept in ill-ventilated rooms, for fear of the cold; and well they may be, with their fashionable style of clothing. But if they were comfortably clothed, it would not harm them to exercise freely in the open air summer or winter. Unhealthful dress brings many a child to a state of invalidism, or, which in many cases may be preferable, to an early death. Thus fashion fills the homes of its slaves with invalids, and our cemeteries with little graves.

Mother, do you want your child to live and wear the bloom of health? Then teach her to dress healthfully. If you love her and desire her good, why do you teach her by your example that it is no sin to mar the human form divine? What reason can you render to the Creator for deforming his handiwork? Turn away from the fashion plates, and study the human organism. We are fearfully and wonderfully made, and we are to present our bodies a living sacrifice to God. How can Christian mothers be worshipers at the shrine of fashion, and yet preserve their loyalty to the God of heaven? It is impossible; "ye cannot serve God and mammon."* You cannot devote your time and talents to the world, and yet keep your mind and body in a condition to do the work committed to you, of training your children for God, and aiding them in a physical development that shall be a blessing to them to the end of life.

Little boys also are dressed so as to leave the lower limbs with far less protection than the upper part of the body. The limbs, being remote from the center of circulation, demand greater protection, instead of less. The veins which convey the blood to the extremities are large, providing for the flow of a sufficient quantity of blood to afford warmth and nutrition. But when the blood is chilled from these parts, the veins contract, and the circulation is retarded. Not only do the extremities suffer from cold, but through lack of nutrition the limbs do not attain their natural development. A good circulation purifies the blood, and secures health; while a poor circulation renders the blood impure, and induces congestion of the vital organs.

Mothers, why not clothe your boys and girls comfortably and properly? Let their dress be simple, loose, and comfortable; clothe their limbs, and especially the ankles, warmly and evenly; then let them go out and exercise in the open air, and live to enjoy health and happiness. It will take moral courage to break away

* Luke 16 : 13.

from the chains of fashion, and dress and educate your children with reference to health ; but the result will abundantly repay all the self-denial and inconvenience occasioned.

Mothers sacrifice to fashion the God-given time which should be devoted to forming the character of their children. Health is impaired by bending over sewing, within doors, shut away from the sunshine and pure air. Opportunities are lost that should be improved in educating the mind, and storing it with useful knowledge. Thus they are not qualified to instruct and train their children for usefulness in this world, or to fit them for the better world. Women are bending their shoulders to a heavy cross. Should Christ demand of them, as his disciples, so great a sacrifice, they would feel that it was indeed too great, and the cross too heavy. Christ requires none of his followers to lift so heavy a burden as that to which they subject themselves as slaves of fashion.

If Christian women would lead out in the good work, and set the example of dressing with neatness and simplicity, and with regard to health, there would be a universal reform. If they would work from an elevated standpoint, they could bring their habits of life into conformity with the laws of their being, and live in obedience to both the physical and the moral requirements of God. Then there would be less money, less nerve force, less physical strength, squandered for artificial decorations, to the sacrifice of natural beauty. We should have more practical wives and mothers, and in many families that are now wretched because of their incorrect ideas of life, there would be a happy change.

The human heart has never been in harmony with the requirements of God. Human reasoning has ever sought to evade or set aside the simple, direct instructions of his word. Those precepts which enjoin self-denial and humility, which require modesty and simplicity in conversation, deportment, and apparel, have, in every age, been disregarded, even by the majority of those who professed to be followers of Christ. The result has ever been the same,— the adoption of the fashions, customs, and principles of the world.

There are few who understand their own hearts. The vain, trifling lovers of fashion may claim to be followers of Christ, but their dress and conversation show what occupies the mind and engages the affections. The outside appearance is an index to the heart. True refinement does not find satisfaction in the adorning of the body for display. A modest, godly woman will dress modestly. Simplicity of apparel always makes a sensible woman appear to the best advantage. A refined, cultured mind will be revealed in the choice of simple and appropriate attire. In the sanctified heart there is no place for thoughts of needless adornment.

Study the fashions less, and the character of Jesus more. The greatest and holiest of men was also the meekest. In his character, majesty and humility were blended. He could summon the hosts of heaven at will; the command of worlds was in his power; yet for our sake he became poor, that we, through his poverty, might be made rich. The attractions of this world, its glory and its pride, had no fascination for him. In the cluster of Christian graces, he made meekness and humility prominent. Christ noticed the devotion to dress, and he cautioned, yea, he commanded, his followers not to bestow too much thought upon it. "Why take ye thought for raiment? Consider the lilies of the field, how they grow; they toil not, neither do they spin; yet I say unto you, That even Solomon in all his glory was not arrayed like one of these." *

The apostles thus describe the adornment that should be sought by Christians: "Whose adorning, let it not be that outward adorning of plaiting the hair, and of wearing of gold, or of putting on of apparel; but let it be the hidden man of the heart, in that which is not corruptible, even the ornament of a meek and quiet spirit, which is in the sight of God of great price."† "In like man-

* Matt. 6:28, 29.   † 1 Peter 3:3.

ner, also, that women adorn themselves in modest apparel, with shamefacedness and sobriety ; not with broidered hair, or gold, or pearls, or costly array ; but (which becometh women professing godliness) with good works." *
Pride and extravagance in dress are sins to which woman is especially prone ; hence these injunctions relate directly to her.

Of how little value are gold or pearls or costly array, when compared with the meekness and loveliness of Christ ! Physical loveliness consists in symmetry — the harmonious proportion of parts ; but spiritual loveliness consists in harmony with Christ — the likeness of our souls to him. The grace of Christ is indeed a priceless adornment. It elevates and ennobles the possessor ; and it also has an influence upon others, attracting them to the Source of light and blessing.

Christian sisters, labor far less to grow into the ever-changing fashions of this age. Study rather the great pattern, Jesus Christ, that you may not grow apart from him. Manifest a determined purpose to abide in the Vine. If you abide in Christ, you will bear much fruit. But as the branch cannot bear fruit of itself, except it abide in the vine, " No more can ye," says Christ, " except ye abide in me." †

The growth of the soul in grace, in purity, in comeliness, is little by little — a progressive work ; but it must go forward unceasingly. The fruit is ever approaching perfection ; the Christian is constantly assimilating the ways and will of Christ. But with many who claim to be Christians there is a painful certainty that they are not progressing heavenward, but are swayed by the customs and practices of the world. Fashions the most unlovely and unhealthful, the most contradictory to the laws of nature, are readily accepted by them. By eagerly beholding these fashions, they become changed to the likeness of what they so much admire. Thus they hasten to adopt the world's standard, where pride and fashion complete in them the transformation which Satan

* 1 Tim. 2:9.   † John 15:14.

delights to see accomplished, and they become unstable as water. The steadfast, silent working of true piety loses its vitality and consistency; "faith, if it hath not works, is dead, being alone."*

There is a dress which every child and youth may innocently seek to obtain. It is the righteousness of the saints. If they will only be as willing and persevering in obtaining this as they are in fashioning their garments after the standard of worldly society, they will very soon be clothed with the righteousness of Christ, and their names will not be blotted out of the book of life. Mothers, as well as youth and children, need to pray, "Create in me a clean heart, O God, and renew a right spirit within me." † This purity of heart and loveliness of spirit are more precious than gold, both for time and for eternity. Only the pure in heart shall see God.

Then, mothers, teach your children, line upon line and precept upon precept, that the righteousness of Christ is the only dress in which they can be admitted into heaven, and that robed in this apparel they will be constantly doing duties in this life which will glorify God.

* James 2 : 17. † Ps. 51 : 10.

GENERAL HYGIENE.

God designed that man should be active and useful; yet the life of many is little more than mere existence. They never brighten the path of others, never bless those around them; on the contrary, they are only a burden. On the side of right their influence is little more than a cipher. Scarcely an instance of disinterested benevolence brightens their life record. No pleasant memory survives them at their death; for there was no true goodness to leave a loving impress, even on the hearts of their friends. Such a life is a sad failure. It is the life of an unfaithful steward, who forgets that his Creator has claims upon him. Selfish interests attract his mind, and lead to forgetfulness of God, and of his purpose in the creation of man.

God placed Adam and Eve in Paradise, and surrounded them with everything that was useful and lovely. He planted for them a beautiful garden, in which no herb or flower or tree was lacking that might be for use or ornament. Paradise delighted their senses, but this was not enough; they must have something to call into play the wonderful machinery of the human system. Had happiness consisted in doing nothing, man in his state of holy innocence would have been left unemployed. But he who formed man, knew what would be for his best happiness, and he no sooner created him than he gave him his appointed work. A life of useful labor is indispensable to the physical, mental, and moral well-being of man.

God has given us all something to do; and in the discharge of various duties, our lives will be made useful, and we shall be blessed. "Not slothful in business,"* is the injunction of the apostle Paul. A person might as well expect a harvest where he has not sown, as to ex-

* Rom. 12:11.

pect to be saved while living in indolence. The race is not always to the swift, nor the battle to the strong, yet "he shall become poor that dealeth with a slack hand."* Those who are diligent in business may not always be prospered ; but drowsiness and idleness are sure to grieve the Spirit of God, and destroy true godliness. A stagnant pool becomes offensive ; but a pure, flowing brook spreads health and gladness over the land.

Riches and idleness are thought by some to be blessings indeed ; but those who are always busy, and who cheerfully go about their daily tasks, are the most happy, and enjoy the best health. The healthful weariness which results from well-regulated labor secures to them the benefits of refreshing sleep. The sentence that man must toil for his daily bread, and the promise of future happiness and glory, both came from the same throne, and both are blessings.

Those who are in possession of wealth and leisure, and yet have no purpose in life, have little to arouse them to either mental or physical activity. Thus many a woman loses her health, and is driven to seek some medical institution for treatment. Here attendants are hired, at great expense, to rub, stretch, and exercise the muscles which have become powerless by inaction. She hires servants, that she may live a life of idleness, and then hires other servants to exercise the muscles enfeebled by disuse. What consummate folly! How much wiser and better for women, young or old, to brave the sneers of fashion's votaries, and obey the dictates of common sense and the laws of life! By the cheerful performance of domestic duties, the idle daughters of our land might become useful and happy members of society. For many, such labor is a more effective and profitable "movement cure" than the best inventions of the physicians.

Young men, as well as young women, often manifest a sad lack of earnest purpose and moral independence. To dress, to smoke, to talk nonsense, and to indulge

* Prov. 10:4.

their passion for amusement, is the ideal of happiness, even with many who profess to be Christians. It is painful to think of the time thus misspent. Hours that should be given to the study of the Scriptures or to active labor for Christ, are worse than wasted. Life was given for a true and holy purpose. It is too precious to be thus squandered. I entreat you who have taken the name of Christ, Examine your hearts, and pass sentence upon yourselves. Do you not love pleasure more than you love God or your fellow-men? There is work to be done; there are souls to save; there are battles to fight; there is a heaven to win. The mind, with all its capabilities, must be strengthened, and stored with the treasures of divine wisdom. In the strength of God you may do noble work for the Master.

God designed that all should be workers. Upon those whose abilities and opportunities are the greatest, rest the heaviest responsibilities; and upon them will fall the heaviest condemnation if they are unfaithful to their trust. Even beasts of burden put to shame the do-nothing, who, endowed with reason and a knowledge of the divine will, refuses to perform his part in God's great plan.

The indolence of the many, occasions the overwork of the few. A large class refuse to think or act for themselves. They have no disposition to step out of the old ruts of prejudice and error; by their perversity they block up the way of advancement, and force the standard-bearers of the right to more heroic efforts in their march forward. Earnest and devoted laborers are failing for want of a helping hand, and are sinking beneath their double burden. Their graves are way-marks along the upward path of reform.

The true glory and joy of life are found only by the working man and woman. Labor brings its own reward, and sweet is the rest that is purchased by the fatigue of a well-spent day. But there is a self-imposed toil which is injurious and utterly unsatisfying. It is that which gratifies unsanctified ambition, which seeks display for notoriety. The love of possession or appearance leads thousands to carry to excess that which, in itself, is lawful—to devote all the strength of mind and body to that which should occupy but a small portion of their time. They bend every energy to the acquisition of wealth or honor, making all other objects secondary; they toil unflinchingly for years to accomplish their purpose; yet when the goal is reached, and the coveted reward secured, it turns to ashes in their grasp; it is a shadow. They have given their life to that which profiteth not.

Yet all the lawful pursuits of life may be safely followed, if the spirit is kept free from selfish hopes and the contamination of deceit and envy. The business life of the Christian should be marked with the same purity that held sway in the workshop of the holy Nazarine. It is the working men and women—those who are willing to bear responsibilities with faith and hope—who find that which is great and good in life. Patient laborers, remember that those were sturdy workmen whom Christ chose from among the fishermen of Galilee and the tent-makers of Corinth, to labor with him in the work of salvation. From these humble men went forth a power that will be felt through all eternity.

The angels are workers; they are ministers of God to the children of men. Those slothful servants who look forward to a heaven of inaction, have false ideas of what constitutes heaven. The Creator has prepared no place for the gratification of sinful indolence. Heaven is a place of interested activity; yet to the weary and heavy laden, to those who have fought the good fight of faith, it will be a glorious rest; for the youth and vigor of immortality will be theirs, and against sin and Satan they will no longer have to contend. To these energetic workers a state of eternal indolence would be irksome. It would be no heaven to them. The path of toil appointed to the Christian on earth may be hard and wearisome, but it is honored by the footprints of the Redeemer, and he is safe who follows in that sacred way.

The idea that those who have overtaxed their mental and physical powers, or who have broken down in body or mind, must suspend activity in order to regain health, is a great error. In a few cases, entire rest for a time may be necessary; but such instances are rare. In most cases the change would be too great to be beneficial.

Those who have broken down by intense mental labor, should have rest from wearing thought; yet to teach them that it is wrong, or even dangerous, for them to exercise their mental powers at all, leads them to view their condition as worse than it really is. They are nervous, and finally become a burden to themselves, as well as to those who care for them. In this state of mind, their recovery is doubtful indeed.

Those who have overtaxed their physical powers should not be advised to forego labor entirely. To shut them away from all exercise would in many cases prevent their restoration to health. The will goes with the labor of the hands; and when the will-power is dormant, the imagination becomes abnormal, so that it is impossible for the sufferer to resist disease. Inactivity is the greatest curse that could come upon one in such a condition.

Nature's fine and wonderful mechanism needs to be constantly exercised in order to be in a condition to accomplish the object for which it was designed. The do-nothing system is a dangerous one in any case. Physical exercise in the direction of useful labor has a happy influence upon the mind, strengthens the muscles, improves the circulation, and gives the invalid the satisfaction of knowing how much he can endure, and that he is not wholly useless in this busy world; whereas, if this is restricted, his attention is turned to himself, and he is in constant danger of exaggerating his difficulties. If invalids would engage in some well-directed physical exercise, using their strength but not abusing it, they would find it an effective agent in their recovery.

When the weather will permit, those who are engaged in sedentary occupations, should, if possible, walk out in the open air every day, summer and winter. The clothing should be suitable, and the feet well protected. **Walking is often more beneficial to health than all the medicine that can be prescribed.** For those who can endure it, walking is preferable to riding; for it brings all the muscles into exercise. The lungs also are forced into healthy action, since it is impossible to walk in the bracing air of a winter morning without inflating them.

Exercise aids the dyspeptic by giving the digestive organs a healthy tone. To engage in deep study or violent exercise immediately after eating, hinders the digestive process; for the vitality of the system, which is needed to carry on the work of digestion, is called away to other parts. But a short walk after a meal, with the head erect and the shoulders back, exercising moderately, is a great benefit. The mind is diverted from self to the beauties of nature. The less the attention is called to the stomach, the better. If you are in constant fear that your food will hurt you, it most assuredly will. Forget your troubles; think of something cheerful.

More people die for want of exercise than from overwork; very many more rust out than wear out. In idleness the blood does not circulate freely, and the changes in the vital fluid, so necessary to health and life, do not take place. The little mouths in the skin, through which the body breathes, become clogged, thus making it impossible to eliminate impurities through that channel. This throws a double burden upon the other excretory organs, and disease is soon produced. Those who accustom themselves to exercising in the open air, generally have a vigorous circulation. Men and women, young or old, who desire health and who would enjoy life, should remember that they cannot have these without a good circulation. Whatever their business or inclinations, they should feel it a religious duty to make wise efforts to overcome the conditions of disease which have kept them in-doors.

MENTAL INFLUENCE.

The Lord has shown me that many who are always complaining, and are apparently feeble, are not in so bad a condition as they think. Some of them have a powerful will, which, if exercised in the right direction, would control the imagination, and be a potent means of resisting disease; but it is too frequently the case that the will is on the wrong side, and stubbornly refuses to yield to reason. That will has settled the matter: invalids they are, and the attention given to invalids they will have, irrespective of the judgment of others.

Thousands are sick and dying around us who might get well and live, if they would. But their imagination controls them. They fear they will be made worse if they engage in any physical labor, when this is just the change they need. They should exercise their will-power and rise above their difficulties, engage in useful employment suited to their strength, and forget that they have aching backs, sides, lungs, and heads.

Let invalids have an exalted aim in life, seeking to be useful and efficient in their own families, and to become useful members of society; let them not require the attention of the whole family to be centered on themselves, nor draw largely upon the sympathies of others; let them do their part in bestowing love and sympathy upon the unfortunate, remembering that each has woes and trials peculiar to himself. In thus blessing others they will realize an abundant blessing themselves.

Those who, so far as it is possible, engage in the work of doing good to others, by giving practical demonstration of their interest in them, are not only relieving the ills of life in helping them to bear burdens, but are at the same time contributing largely to their own health of soul and body. Doing good is a work that benefits both giver and receiver. If you forget self in your interest for others, you gain a victory over your own infirmities. The pleasure of doing good animates the mind, and vibrates through the whole body. If thou clothe the naked, and "bring the poor that are cast out to thy house," and "deal thy bread to the hungry," "then shall thy light break forth as the morning, and thine health shall spring forth speedily."

IMPORTANCE OF PURE AIR.

Some invalids refuse to be convinced of the great importance of having a constant supply of pure air. For fear of taking cold, they willfully persist in living from year to year in an atmosphere almost destitute of vitality. It is impossible for such to have a healthy circulation. The skin is debilitated, and they become sensitive to any change in the atmosphere. The first suggestion of cold brings out additional clothing, and the heat of the room is increased. The next day they require a little more heat, and a little more clothing, in order to feel perfectly warm, and thus they humor every changing feeling until they have but little vitality left. If those who can, would engage in some active employment, instead of adding to their clothing or raising the temperature of an already overheated room, they would generally forget their chilly sensations, and would receive no harm. For feeble lungs, an overheated atmosphere is very injurious.

Winter is a season to be dreaded by those who are obliged to be with these invalids. It is not only winter out-of-doors, but dreary in-doors. Under the plea that the air affects their lungs and head, these victims of a diseased imagination shut themselves up in the house, and close the windows. They expect to take cold from the least exposure, and they do. "Have we not proved it?" they will argue, and no amount of reasoning can make them believe that they do not understand the philosophy of the whole matter. It is true that they do take cold when exposed; but it is because their course has made them as tender as babies, and they cannot endure anything. Yet they live on with windows and doors closed, hovering over the stove, and enjoying their misery.

* Isa. 58 : 7, 8.

Why will not such try the effect of judicious out-door exercise?

Many have been taught that night air is positively injurious to health, and therefore must be excluded from their rooms. One autumn evening I was traveling in a crowded car. The exhalations from so many lungs and bodies rendered the atmosphere very impure, and caused a sickening sensation to come over me. I raised my window, and was enjoying the fresh air, when a lady in earnest, imploring tones, cried out, "Do put down that window! You will take cold and be sick; the night air is so unhealthful!" I replied, "Madam, we have no other air than night air, in this car or out of it. If you refuse to breathe the night air, you must stop breathing." In the cool of the evening it may be necessary to guard against chilliness by extra clothing; but there should be a free circulation of pure air through the room during sleeping hours. The free air of heaven, by day or night, is one of the richest blessings we can enjoy.

Fresh air will purify the blood, refresh the body, and help to make it strong and healthy. The invigoration produced will be reflected upon the mind, imparting to it tone and clearness, as well as a degree of composure and serenity. It gives a healthful stimulus to the appetite, renders the digestion of food more perfect, and induces sound, sweet sleep. Living in close, ill-ventilated rooms, weakens the system, makes the mind gloomy, the skin sallow, and the circulation feeble; the blood moves sluggishly, digestion is retarded, and the system is rendered peculiarly sensitive to cold. One should so accustom himself to fresh, cool air that he will not be affected by slight changes of temperature. Of course he should be careful not to sit in a draft or in a cold room when weary, or when in a perspiration.

Many labor under the mistaken idea that if they have taken cold they must carefully exclude the outside air, and increase the temperature of the room until it is excessively hot. But the system of one suffering with cold is deranged, the pores are closed by waste matter, and there is more or less inflammation of the internal organs, because the blood has been chilled back from the surface, and thrown upon them. At this time, of all others, the lungs should not be deprived of pure air. Judicious exercise would induce the blood to the surface, and thus relieve the internal organs. The power of the will is a great help in resisting cold, and giving energy to the nervous system. To deprive the lungs of air, is like depriving the stomach of food. Air is the food that God has provided for the lungs. Welcome it; cultivate a love for it, as a precious boon of heaven.

HOME HYGIENE.

One of the most prolific sources of disease is the transgression of the laws of life in regard to personal habits. Order and cleanliness are laws of heaven. The directions given to Moses when the Lord was about to declare his law upon Mount Sinai, were very strict in this respect. "And the Lord said unto Moses, Go unto the people, and sanctify them to-day and to-morrow, and let them wash their clothes."* They were directed to do this lest there should be impurity about them as they should come before him. He is a God of order, and he requires order and cleanliness in his people.

The children of Israel were in no case to allow any impurities to remain upon their clothing or upon themselves. Those who had any personal uncleanness were to be shut out of the camp until the evening, and then were required to cleanse themselves and their clothing before they could return. They were also commanded to carry all their refuse to a great distance from the camp. And this was a sanitary measure, as well as a religious regulation. The Lord requires no less of his people now than he did anciently. A neglect of cleanliness will induce disease. Sickness does not come without a cause. Violent epidemics of fevers have occurred in villages and cities that were considered perfectly healthful, and these have

* Ex. 19 : 10.

resulted in death or broken constitutions. In many instances the premises of the very ones who fell victims to these epidemics, contained the agents of destruction which sent forth deadly poison into the atmosphere, to be inhaled by the family and the neighborhood. It is astonishing to witness the prevailing ignorance relative to the effects which slackness and recklessness produce upon health.

When Lord Palmerston, premier of England, was petitioned by the Scottish clergy to appoint a day of fasting and prayer to avert the cholera, he replied, "Cleanse and disinfect your streets and houses, promote cleanliness and health among the poor, and see that they are plentifully supplied with good food and raiment, and employ right sanitary measures generally, and you will have no occasion to fast and pray. Nor will the Lord hear your prayers while these, his preventives, remain unheeded."

It is not God who has brought upon us the many woes which mortals now inherit. Our own folly has led us to deprive ourselves of things that are precious, of the blessings which, if properly used, are of inestimable value in the maintenance of health. If you would have your home sweet and inviting, make it bright with air and sunshine. Remove your heavy curtains, open the windows, throw back the blinds, and enjoy the rich sunlight, even if it be at the expense of the colors of your carpets.

Some houses are furnished expensively, more to gratify pride than for the comfort, convenience, or health of the family. The best rooms are kept closed and dark, lest the light might injure the rich furniture, fade the carpets, or tarnish the picture frames. When visitors are permitted to be seated in these precious rooms, they are in danger of taking cold because of the damp atmosphere pervading them. Parlor bedrooms are kept closed for the same reasons. Sleeping-rooms should be large, and so arranged as to have a free circulation of air day and night. Those who have slept in an ill-ventilated room awake feeling feverish and exhausted. This is because the vital air was excluded, and the whole system suffers in consequence.

Whoever occupies beds which have not been freely exposed to the air and sunlight, does so at the risk of health, and often even of life itself. There should be a circulation of air and an abundance of light through every apartment of the house for several hours each day. If you have God's presence, and possess earnest, loving hearts, then a humble home, made bright with air and sunshine, and cheerful with the welcome of unselfish hospitality, will be to your family and the weary traveler a heaven below.

Upon rising in the morning, most persons would be benefited by taking a sponge or hand bath. This will remove all impurities from the skin, and keep it moist and supple, thereby aiding the circulation. Persons in health should on no account neglect frequent bathing. Whether a person is sick or well, respiration is rendered more free and full by bathing. The mind and body are alike invigorated. The muscles become more flexible, every faculty of the intellect is made brighter. The bath is a soother of the nerves. Instead of increasing the liability of taking cold, it fortifies against cold, because it improves the circulation; the blood is brought to the surface, and a more easy and regular flow of the vital fluid is obtained.

A yard beautified with scattering trees and some shrubbery, at a proper distance from the house, has a happy influence upon the family, and, if well taken care of, will prove no injury to the health. But shade trees and shrubbery close and dense around a house, make it unhealthful; for they prevent the free circulation of air, and shut out the rays of the sun. In consequence, a dampness gathers in the house, especially in wet seasons. Those who occupy the sleeping-rooms are troubled with rheumatism, neuralgia, and lung complaints. Then the great quantities of fallen leaves, if not removed immediately, decay, and poison the atmosphere. Dwellings, if possible, should be built on high ground. If a house is built where the water will settle around it, remaining for a time and slowly drying away, there is a poisonous miasma continually rising from the damp ground, which breeds sore throat, fevers, ague, or lung diseases.

Many expect that God will keep them from sickness merely because they ask him to do so. But the prayers of those who do not regard the laws of life, God cannot answer, because their faith is not made perfect by works. When we do all on our part to insure health, then we may expect that good results will follow, and we can ask God in faith to bless our efforts. And he will answer our prayer, if his name can be glorified thereby. But let all understand that they have a work to do. God will not work in a miraculous manner to preserve the health of persons who are, by their careless inattention to the laws of health, taking a sure course to make themselves sick.

The Lord has shown me that Sabbath-keepers as a rule labor too hard, without allowing themselves change or periods of rest. Recreation is needful to those who engage in physical labor, and is still more essential for those whose work is principally mental. It is not essential to our salvation nor for the glory of God to keep the mind laboring constantly and excessively, even upon religious themes. There are amusements, such as card-playing, dancing, theater-going, etc., which we cannot approve, because Heaven condemns them. They open the door to great evils. By their exciting tendency they produce in some minds a passion for gambling and dissipation. All such amusements should be condemned by Christians, and something perfectly harmless should be substituted in their place. There are modes of recreation which are highly beneficial to both mind and body. An enlightened, discriminating mind will find abundant means for entertainment and diversion from sources not only innocent, but instructive. Recreation in the open air, and the contemplation of the works of God in nature, will be of the highest benefit.

FALSE IMPRESSIONS CONCERNING EXPERIENCE.

EXPERIENCE is said to be the best teacher. Genuine experience is indeed superior to mere theoretical knowledge, but many have an erroneous idea as to what constitutes experience. Real experience is gained by a variety of careful experiments, made with the mind free from prejudice, uncontrolled by previously established opinions and habits. The results are marked with careful solicitude, and an anxious desire to learn, to improve, and to reform on every point that is not in harmony with physical and moral laws.

That which many term experience is not experience at all; it has resulted from mere habit, or from a course of indulgence, thoughtlessly and often ignorantly followed. There has not been a fair trial by actual experiment and thorough investigation, with a knowledge of the principles involved in the action. Experience which is opposed to natural law,— which is in conflict with the unchangeable principles of nature,— is not to be relied upon. Superstition arising from a diseased imagination is often arrayed in opposition to reason and to scientific principles. To many a person, the idea that others may gainsay what he has learned by experience, seems folly, and even cruelty itself. But there are more errors received and held through false ideas of experience than from any other cause. There are many invalids to-day who will ever remain such because they cannot be convinced that their experience is not to be relied upon.

Erroneous habits and customs gird men and women as with iron bands, and they too often justify themselves in these customs by what they term experience. Many of the grossest habits are cherished under this plea.

Many fail to reach that physical, mental, and moral development to which they might attain, because they cling to an experience that is opposed to the plainest revealed facts. Men and women whose wrong habits have destroyed their health, and broken down their constitution, will be found recommending their experience as safe for others to follow, when it is this very experience that has robbed them of health and vitality. When you seek to instruct them, they defend their course by referring to their experience.

Here is where we have met the greatest difficulties in religious matters. The plainest facts may be presented, the clearest truths, sustained by the word of God, may be brought before the mind; but the ear and the heart are closed, and the all-convincing argument is, "my experience." Some will say, "The Lord has blessed me in believing and doing as I have; therefore I cannot be in error." "My experience" is clung to, and the most elevating, sanctifying truths of the Bible are rejected.

Balaam inquired of God if he might curse Israel. He was anxious that the permission might be given, because he had the promise of great reward. But God said, "Thou shalt not go." Balaam was urged the second time, by messengers more honorable than the first, and greater inducements were offered. He had been shown the will of the Lord in this matter, but he was so eager for the reward that he ventured to ask God a second time, and the Lord permitted him to go. Then he had a wonderful experience; but who would wish to have such an experience?

Many examples might be given to show how people have been deceived by relying upon what they supposed to be their experience.

CONSULTING SPIRITUALIST
PHYSICIANS.

FROM time to time I have received letters from both ministers and lay-members of the church, inquiring if I think it wrong to consult spiritualist and clairvoyant physicians. So numerous are these agents of Satan becoming, and so general is the practice of seeking council from them, that it seems needful to utter words of warning.

God has placed it in our power to obtain a knowledge of the laws of health. He has made it a duty to preserve our physical powers in the best possible condition, that we may render to him acceptable service. Those who refuse to improve the light and knowledge that have been mercifully placed within their reach, are rejecting one of the means which God has granted them to promote spiritual as well as physical life. They are placing themselves where they will be exposed to the delusions of Satan.

Not a few in this Christian age and Christian nation resort to evil spirits, rather than trust to the power of the living God. The mother, watching by the sick-bed of her child, exclaims, "I can do no more. Is there no physician who has power to restore my child?" She is told of the wonderful cures performed by some clairvoyant or magnetic healer, and she trusts her dear one to his charge, placing it as verily in the hands of Satan as if he were standing by her side. In many instances the future life of the child is controlled by a satanic power which it seems impossible to break.

I have heard a mother pleading with an infidel physician to save the life of her child; but when I entreated her to seek help from the Great Physician, who is able to

save to the uttermost all who come to him in faith, she
turned away with impatience.

When Ahaziah, king of Israel, was sick, "he sent messengers, and said unto them, Go, inquire of Baal-zebub,
the god of Ekron, whether I shall recover from this disease." On the way they met Elijah, and instead of a
message from the idol, the king heard the awful denun-
ciation from the God of Israel, "Thou shalt not come
down from that bed on which thou art gone up, but shalt
surely die."* It was Christ that bade Elijah speak these
words to the apostate king. Jehovah Immanuel had cause
to be greatly displeased at Ahaziah's impiety. What had
Christ not done to win the hearts of Israel, and to inspire
them with unwavering confidence in himself? For ages
he had visited his people with manifestations of the most
condescending kindness and unexampled love. From the
time of the patriarchs, he had shown how his "delights
were with the sons of men."† He had been a very present help to all who sought him in sincerity. "In all their
affliction he was afflicted, and the Angel of his presence
saved them: in his love and in his pity he redeemed
them."‡ Yet Israel had revolted from God, and turned
for help to the Lord's worst enemy.

The Hebrews were the only nation favored with a
knowledge of the true God. When the king of Israel
sent to inquire of a pagan oracle, he proclaimed to the
heathen that he had more confidence in their idols than
in the God of his people, the Creator of the heavens and
the earth. In the same manner do those who profess to
have a knowledge of God's word dishonor him when they
turn from the source of strength and wisdom, to ask help
or counsel from the powers of darkness. If God's wrath
was kindled by such a course on the part of a wicked,
idolatrous king, how must he regard a similar course pur-
sued by those who profess to be his servants?

Many are unwilling to put forth the needed effort to
obtain a knowledge of the laws of life and the simple

*2 Kings 1:4.   †Prov. 8:31.   ‡Isa. 63:9.

means to be employed for the restoration of health. They do not place themselves in right relation to life. When sickness is the result of their transgression of natural law, they do not seek to correct their errors, and then ask the blessing of God, but they resort to the physicians. If they recover health, they give to drugs and doctors all the honor. They are ever ready to idolize human power and wisdom, seeming to know no other god than the creature,—dust and ashes.

It is not safe to trust to physicians who have not the fear of God before them. Without the influence of divine grace, the hearts of men are "deceitful above all things, and desperately wicked."* Self-aggrandizement is their aim. Under cover of the medical profession, what iniquities have been practiced, what delusions supported! The physician may claim to possess great wisdom and marvelous skill, while at the same time his character is abandoned, and his practice contrary to the laws of health. The Lord our God assures us that he is waiting to be gracious; he invites us to call upon him in the day of trouble. Furthermore, the teaching of these physicians is continually leading away from the principles God has given us in regard to health, especially on the diet question. They say we are not living as we ought, and prescribe changes that are contrary to the light God has sent. Brethren, how can the Lord let his blessing rest upon us when we are going right upon the enemy's ground?

Why is it that men are so unwilling to trust Him who created man, and who can, by a touch, a word, a look, heal all manner of disease? Who is more worthy of our confidence than the One who has made so great a sacrifice for our redemption? Our Lord has given us definite instruction, through the apostle James, as to our duty in case of sickness. When human help fails, God will be the helper of his people. "Is any sick among you? let him call for the elders of the church, and let

* Jer. 17: 9.

them pray over him, anointing him with oil in the name of the Lord; and the prayer of faith shall save the sick, and the Lord shall raise him up."* If the professed followers of Christ would, with purity of heart, exercise as much faith in the promises of God as they repose in satanic agencies, they would realize, in soul and body, the life-giving power of the Holy Spirit.

God has granted to this people great light, yet we are not placed beyond the reach of temptation. Who among us are seeking help from the gods of Ekron? Look on this picture—a picture not drawn from imagination. In how many, even among Seventh-day Adventists, may its leading characteristics be seen! An invalid, apparently very conscientious, yet bigoted and self-sufficient, freely avows his contempt for the laws of life and health, which divine mercy has led us as a people to accept. His food must be prepared in a manner to satisfy his morbid cravings. Rather than sit at a table where wholesome food is provided, he will patronize restaurants, because he can there indulge appetite without restraint. A fluent advocate of temperance, he disregards its foundation principles. He wants relief, but refuses to obtain it at the price of self-denial. That man is worshiping at the shrine of perverted appetite. He is an idolater. The powers, which, sanctified and ennobled, might be employed to honor God, are weakened, and rendered of little service. An irritable temper, a confused brain, and unstrung nerves are among the results of his disregard of nature's laws. He is inefficient and unreliable. Whoever has the courage and honesty to warn him of danger, thereby incurs his displeasure. The slightest remonstrance or opposition is sufficient to rouse his combative spirit. But now an opportunity is presented to seek help from one whose power comes through the medium of witchcraft. To this source he applies with eagerness, freely expending time and money in the hope of securing the proffered boon. He is deceived, infatuated. The sorcerer's power is made

* James 5 : 14, 15.

the theme of praise, and others are influenced to seek his aid. Thus the God of Israel is dishonored, while Satan's power is revered and exalted.

In the name of Christ I would address his professed followers: Abide in the faith which you have received from the beginning. "Shun profane and vain babblings."* Instead of putting your trust in witchcraft, have faith in the living God. Cursed is the path that leads to Endor or to Ekron. The feet will stumble and fall that venture upon this forbidden ground. There is a God in Israel, with whom is deliverance for all who are oppressed. Righteousness is the foundation of his throne.

There is danger in departing in the least from the Lord's instruction. When we deviate from the plain path of duty, a train of circumstances will arise that seems irresistibly to draw us farther and farther from the right. Needless intimacies with those who have no respect for God will seduce us ere we are aware. The fear of offending worldly friends will deter us from expressing our gratitude to God, or acknowledging our dependence upon him.

We must keep close to the word of God. We need its warnings and encouragement, its threatenings and promises. We need the perfect example given only in the life and character of our Saviour. Angels of God will preserve his people while they walk in the path of duty; but there is no assurance of such protection for those who deliberately venture upon Satan's ground. An agent of the great deceiver will say and do anything to gain his object. It matters little whether he calls himself a spiritualist, an "electric physician," or a "magnetic healer." By specious pretenses he wins the confidence of the unwary. He pretends to read the life history, and to understand all the difficulties and afflictions of those who resort to him. Disguising himself as an angel of light, while the blackness of the pit is in his heart, he manifests great interest in women who seek his counsel. He

* 2 Tim. 2 : 16.

tells them that all their troubles are due to an unhappy marriage. This may be too true, but such counsel does not better their condition. He tells them that they need love and sympathy. Pretending great interest in their welfare, he casts a spell over his unsuspecting victims, charming them as the serpent charms the trembling bird. Soon they are completely in his power, and sin, disgrace, and ruin are the terrible sequel.

Our only safety is in preserving the ancient landmarks. "To the law and to the testimony; if they speak not according to this word, it is because there is no light in them." *

* Isa. 8 : 20.

OUR PRESENT WORK.

WE should educate ourselves, not only to live in harmony with the laws of health, but to teach others the better way. Many, even of those who profess to believe the special truths for this time, are lamentably ignorant with regard to health and temperance. They need to be educated, line upon line, precept upon precept. The subject must be kept fresh before them. This matter must not be passed over as non-essential; for nearly every family needs to be stirred up on the question. The conscience must be aroused to the duty of practicing the principles of true reform. God requires that his people shall be temperate in all things. Unless they practice true temperance, they will not, they cannot, be susceptible to the sanctifying influence of the truth.

Our ministers should become intelligent upon this question. They should not ignore it, nor be turned aside by those who call them extremists. Let them find out what constitutes true health reform, and teach its principles, both by precept and by a quiet, consistent example. At our large gatherings, instruction should be given upon health and temperance. Seek to arouse the intellect and the conscience. Bring into service all the talent at command, and follow up the work with publications upon the subject. "Educate, educate, educate," is the message that has been impressed upon me.

In all our missions, women of intelligence should have charge of the domestic arrangements,— women who know how to prepare food nicely and healthfully. The table should be abundantly supplied with food of the best quality. If any have a perverted taste that craves tea, coffee, condiments, and unhealthful dishes, enlighten them. Seek to arouse the conscience. Set before them the principles of the Bible upon hygiene. Where plenty of good milk and fruit can be obtained, there is rarely any excuse for eating animal food; it is not necessary to take the life of any of God's creatures to supply our ordinary needs. In certain cases of illness or exhaustion it may be thought best to use some meat, but great care should be taken to secure the flesh of healthy animals. It has come to be a very serious question whether it is safe to use flesh-food at all in this age of the world. It would be better never to eat meat than to use the flesh of animals that are not healthy. When I could not obtain the food I needed, I have sometimes eaten a little meat; but I am becoming more and more afraid of it.

When God led the children of Israel out of Egypt, it was his purpose to establish them in the land of Canaan a pure, happy, healthy people. Let us look at the means by which he would accomplish this. He subjected them to a course of discipline, which, had it been cheerfully followed, would have resulted in good, both to themselves and to their posterity. He removed flesh-food from them in a great measure. He had granted them flesh in answer to their clamors, just before reaching Sinai, but it was furnished for only one day. God might have provided flesh as easily as manna, but a restriction was placed upon the people for their good. It was his purpose to supply them with food better suited to their wants than the feverish diet to which many of them had been accustomed in Egypt. The perverted appetite was to be brought into a more healthy state, that they might enjoy the food originally provided for man,—the fruits of the earth, which God gave to Adam and Eve in Eden.

Had they been willing to deny appetite in obedience to his restrictions, feebleness and disease would have been unknown among them. Their descendants would have possessed physical and mental strength. They would have had clear perceptions of truth and duty, keen discrimination, and sound judgment. But they were unwilling to submit to God's requirements, and they failed to reach the standard he had set for them, and to receive the blessings that might have been theirs. They murmured at God's restrictions, and lusted after the flesh-pots of Egypt. God let them have flesh, but it proved a curse to them.

Again and again I have been shown that God is trying to lead us back, step by step, to his original design,—that man should subsist upon the natural products of the earth. Among those who are waiting for the coming of the Lord, meat-eating will eventually be done away; flesh will cease to form a part of their diet. We should ever keep this end in view, and endeavor to work steadily toward it. I cannot think that in the practice of flesh-eating we are in harmony with the light which God has been pleased to give us. All who are connected with our health institutions especially should be educating themselves to subsist on fruits, grains, and vegetables. If we move from principle in these things, if we as Christian reformers educate our own taste, and bring our diet to God's plan, then we may exert an influence upon others in this matter, which will be pleasing to God.

One reason why many have become discouraged in practicing health reform is that they have not learned how to cook so that proper food, simply prepared, would supply the place of the diet to which they have been accustomed. They become disgusted with the poorly prepared dishes, and next we hear them say that they have tried the health reform, and cannot live in that way. Many attempt to follow out meager instructions in health reform, and make such sad work that it results in injury to digestion, and in discouragement to all concerned in the attempt. You profess to be health reformers, and for this very reason you should become good cooks. Those who can avail themselves of the advantages of properly conducted hygienic cooking-schools, will find it a great benefit, both in their own practice and in teaching others.

Do not catch hold of isolated ideas and make them a test, criticising others whose practice may not agree with your opinion; but study the subject broadly and deeply, and seek to bring your own ideas and practices into perfect harmony with the principles of true Christian temperance.

There are many who try to correct the lives of others by attacking what they regard as wrong habits. They go to those whom they think in error, and point out their defects, but do not seek to direct the mind to true principles. Such a course often comes far short of securing the desired results. When we make it evident that we are trying to correct others, we too often arouse their combativeness, and do more harm than good. And there is danger to the reprover also. He who takes it upon himself to correct others, is likely to cultivate a habit of fault-finding, and soon his whole interest will be in picking flaws and finding defects. Do not watch others, to pick at their faults or expose their errors. Educate them to better habits by the power of your own example.

Let it ever be kept before the mind that the great object of hygienic reform is to secure the highest possible development of mind and soul and body. All the laws of nature—which are the laws of God—are designed for our good. Obedience to them will promote our happiness in this life, and will aid us in a preparation for the life to come.

There is something better to talk about than the faults and weaknesses of others. Talk of God and his wonderful works. Study into the manifestations of his love and wisdom in all the works of nature. Study that marvelous organism, the human system, and the laws by which it is governed. Those who perceive the evidences of God's love, who understand something of the wisdom and beneficence of his laws, and the blessings that result from obedience, will come to regard their duties and obligations from an altogether different point of view. Instead of looking upon an observance of the laws of health as a matter of sacrifice or self-denial, they will regard it, as it really is, as an inestimable blessing.

A great amount of good can be done by enlightening all to whom we have access, as to the best means, not only of curing the sick, but of preventing disease and suffering. The physician who endeavors to enlighten his patients as to the nature and causes of their maladies, and to teach them how to avoid disease, may have up-hill work; but if he is a conscientious reformer, he will talk plainly of the ruinous effects of self-indulgence in eating, drinking, and dressing, of the overtaxation of the vital forces that has brought his patients where they are. He will not increase the evil by administering drugs till exhausted nature gives up the struggle, but will teach the patients how to form correct habits, and to aid nature in her work of restoration by a wise use of her own simple remedies.

In all our health institutions, it should be made a special feature of the work to give instruction in regard to the laws of health. The principles of health reform should be carefully and thoroughly set before all, both patients and helpers. This work requires moral courage; for while many will profit by such efforts, others will be offended. But the true disciple of Christ, he whose mind is in harmony with the mind of God, while constantly learning, will be teaching as well, leading the minds of others upward, away from the prevailing errors of the world.

Much of the prejudice that prevents, the truth of the third angel's message from reaching the hearts of the people, might be removed if more attention were given to health reform. When people become interested in this subject, the way is often prepared for the entrance of other truths. If they see that we are intelligent with regard to health, they will be more ready to believe that we are sound in Bible doctrines.

This branch of the Lord's work has not received due attention, and through this neglect much has been lost. If the church would manifest a greater interest in the reforms through which God himself is seeking to fit them for his coming, their influence would be far greater than it now is. God has spoken to his people, and he designs that they shall hear and obey his voice. Although the health reform is not the third angel's message, it is closely connected with it. Those who proclaim the message should teach health reform also. It is a subject that we must understand, in order to be prepared for the events that are close upon us, and it should have a prominent place. Satan and his agents are seeking to hinder this work of reform, and will do all they can to perplex and burden those who heartily engage in it. Yet none should be discouraged at this, or cease their efforts because of it. The prophet Isaiah speaks thus of one characteristic of Christ: "He shall not fail nor be discouraged, till he have set judgment in the earth."* Then let not his followers talk of failure or discouragement, but remember the price paid to rescue man that he might not perish, but have eternal life.

* Isa. 42 : 4.

MENTAL INEBRIATES.

WHAT shall our children read? is a serious question, and demands a serious answer. I am troubled to see, in Christian families, periodicals and newspapers containing continued stories that leave no impress of good upon the mind. I have watched those whose taste for fiction has been thus cultivated. They have had the privilege of listening to the truths of God's word, of becoming acquainted with the reasons of our faith; but they have grown to mature years destitute of true piety. These dear youth need so much to put into their character-building the very best material,—the love and fear of God and a knowledge of Christ. But many have not an intelligent understanding of the truth as it is in Jesus. The mind is feasted upon sensational stories. They live in an unreal world, and are unfitted for the practical duties of life. I have observed children allowed to come up in this way. Whether at home or abroad, they are either restless or dreamy, and are unable to converse, save upon the most common-place subjects. The nobler faculties, those adapted to higher pursuits, have been degraded to the contemplation of trivial, or worse than trivial subjects, until their possessor has become satisfied with such topics, and scarcely has power to reach anything higher. Religious thought and conversation has become distasteful. The mental food for which he has acquired a relish, is contaminating in its effects, and leads to impure and sensual thoughts. I have felt sincere pity for these souls as I have considered how much they are losing by neglecting opportunities to gain a knowledge of Christ, in whom our hopes of eternal life are centered. How much precious time is wasted, in which they might be studying the pattern of true goodness.

I am personally acquainted with some who have lost the healthy tone of the mind through wrong habits of reading. They go through life with a diseased imagination, magnifying every little grievance. Things which a sound, sensible mind would not notice, become to them unendurable trials, insurmountable obstacles. To them, life is in constant shadow.

Those who have indulged the habit of racing through exciting stories, are crippling their mental strength, and disqualifying themselves for vigorous thought and research. There are men and women now in the decline of life who have never recovered from the effects of intemperate reading. The habit, formed in early years, has grown with their growth and strengthened with their strength; and their efforts to overcome it, though determined, have been only partially successful. Many have never recovered their original vigor of mind. All attempts to become practical Christians end with the desire. They cannot be truly Christ-like, and continue to feed the mind upon this class of literature. Nor is the physical effect less disastrous. The nervous system is unnecessarily taxed by this passion for reading. In some cases, youth, and even those of mature age, have been afflicted with paralysis from no other cause than excess in reading. The mind was kept under constant excitement, until the delicate machinery of the brain became so weakened that it could not act, and paralysis was the result.

When an appetite for exciting, sensational stories is cultivated, the moral taste becomes perverted, and the mind is unsatisfied unless constantly fed upon this trashy, unwholesome food. I have seen young ladies, professed followers of Christ, who were really unhappy unless they had on hand some new novel or story-paper. The mind craved stimulation, as the drunkard craves intoxicating drink. These youth manifested no spirit of devotion; no heavenly light was shed upon their associates, to lead them to the fount of knowledge. They had no deep religious experience. If this class of reading had not been constantly before them, there might have been some hope of their reforming; but they craved it, and would have it.

I am pained to see young men and women thus ruining their usefulness in this life, and failing to obtain an experience that will prepare them for an eternal life in heavenly society. We can find no more fit name for them than "mental inebriates." Intemperate habits of reading exert a pernicious influence upon the brain as surely as does intemperance in eating or drinking.

The best way to prevent the growth of evil is to preoccupy the soil. The greatest care and watchfulness is needed in cultivating the mind and sowing therein the precious seeds of Bible truth. The Lord, in his great mercy, has revealed to us in the Scriptures the rules of holy living. He tells us the sins to shun; he explains to us the plan of salvation, and points out the way to heaven. He has inspired holy men to record, for our benefit, instruction concerning the dangers that beset our path, and how to escape them. Those who obey his injunction to search the Scriptures will not be ignorant of these things. Amid the perils of the last days, every member of the church should understand the reasons of his hope and faith,—reasons which are not difficult of comprehension. There is enough to occupy the mind, if we would grow in grace and in the knowledge of our Lord Jesus Christ.

We are finite, but we are to have a sense of the infinite. The mind must be brought into exercise in contemplating God and his wonderful plan for our salvation. The soul will thus be lifted above the mere earthly and common-place, and fixed upon that which is ennobling and eternal. The thought that we are in God's world, in the presence of the great Creator of the universe, who made man after his own likeness, will lead the mind into broad, exalted fields for meditation. The thought that God's eye is watching over us, that he loves us, and cared so much for us as to give his dearly beloved Son to redeem us, that we might not miserably perish, is a great one; and he who opens his heart to the acceptance and contemplation of themes like these, will never be satisfied with trivial, sensational subjects.

If the Bible were studied as it should be, men would become strong in intellect. The subjects treated upon in the word of God, the dignified simplicity of its utterance, the noble themes which it presents to the mind, develop faculties in man which cannot otherwise be developed. In the Bible, a boundless field is opened for the imagination. The student will come from a contemplation of its grand themes, from association with its lofty imagery, more pure and elevated in thought and feeling than if he had spent the time in reading any work of mere human origin, to say nothing of those of a trifling character. Youthful minds fail to reach their noblest development when they neglect the highest source of wisdom,— the word of God. The reason why we have so few men of good mind, of stability and solid worth, is, that God is not feared, God is not loved, the principles of religion are not carried out in the life as they should be.

God would have us avail ourselves of every means of cultivating and strengthening our intellectual powers. We were created for a higher, nobler existence than the life that now is. This time is one of preparation for the future, immortal life. Where can be found grander themes for contemplation, a more interesting subject for thought, than the sublime truths unfolded in the Bible? These truths will do a mighty work for man, if he will but follow what they teach. But how little the Bible is studied! Every unimportant thing is dwelt upon in preference to its themes. If the Bible were read more, if its truths were better understood, we should be a far more enlightened and intelligent people. Energy is imparted to the soul by searching its pages. Angels from the world of light stand by the side of the earnest seeker after truth, to impress and illuminate his mind. He who is dark of understanding may find light through an acquaintance with the Scriptures.

SOCIAL PURITY.

"BLESSED are the pure in heart; for they shall see God." * Man has fallen, and the work of his life-time, be it longer or shorter, must be to recover through Christ what he has lost by sin,— the likeness to the divine. This work requires a thorough transformation of soul, body, and spirit. God mercifully sends rays of light to show man his true condition; but if he will not walk in the light, it is manifest that he takes pleasure in darkness. He avoids the light, lest his deeds should be reproved.

A picture of the terrible condition of the world has been presented before me. Immorality abounds on every hand. Licentiousness is the prevailing sin of this age. Never did vice lift its deformed head with such boldness as now, and by its strength and prevalence the lovers of virtue are almost discouraged. Unless man has more than human strength to resist the current of evil, he will be overcome, and borne down to perdition.

But the mind does not come down in a moment from purity and holiness to depravity, corruption, and crime. To degrade to the brutal and satanic those who are formed in the image of God, takes time. By beholding we become changed. Though formed in the image of his Maker, man can so accustom himself to evil that the sin which he once loathed will become pleasant to him. As he ceases to watch and pray, he ceases to guard the citadel — the heart — and is betrayed into sin and crime. Constant war against the carnal mind must be maintained; and we must be aided by the refining influence of the grace of God, which will attract the mind upward, and habituate it to meditate upon pure and holy things.

A large class of the human beings we everywhere meet are a curse to the world. They live only for self-indulgence, and are given up, soul and body, to corrupt and dis-

* Matt. 5 : 8.　　　　　　　(127)

solute habits.   What a terrible rebuke are such lives to the mothers who have worshiped at fashion's shrine, and have neglected to cultivate their own mind and to form their own character after the divine Pattern ; and who have thus been unprepared to fulfill the sacred trust committed to them, — to bring up their children in the nurture and admonition of the Lord.

It is almost impossible to arouse those who need to be awakened, to any just sense of the power which Satan has over the mind.   Neither are they aware of the corruption teeming all around them.   Satan has blinded them, and lulled them to carnal security.   Iniquity abounds, and it is not confined merely to the unbeliever and the scoffer : many who profess the religion of Christ are also guilty. Their love is waxing cold.   Alas! how few there are, even among professed Christians, who do the right for its own sake, — who will shun evil when public opinion does not restrain them!

In the battle with inward corruption and outward temptation, even the wise and powerful Solomon was vanquished. His life began under favorable auspices.   He was beloved of God ; and, had virtue been preserved, his life might have closed in prosperity and honor.   But he surrendered this special grace to lustful passion.   In his youth he trusted in God, and looked to him for guidance ; and the Lord gave him power and wisdom that astonished the world. His fame reached to all lands.   But when he began to descend the declivity of life, he yielded principle, thus placing himself in the current of evil, and separating himself from God, the foundation and source of his strength ; he lost his firmness of character, and wavered, like a giddy youth, between right and wrong.   His love of women was his sin.   This passion he did not control in his manhood, and it proved a snare to him.   He took many wives, some of whom were daughters of heathen kings ; and they led him into idolatry.   In his youth, wisdom had been more precious to him than the golden wedge of Ophir. But, alas! lustful passions gained the victory.   He was deceived and ruined by women. What a lesson is here taught! What a demonstration of the need of strength from God to the very last! It is not safe to permit the least departure from strict integrity.

"Let not sin, therefore, reign in your mortal body, that ye should obey it in the lusts thereof. Neither yield ye your members as instruments of unrighteousness unto sin; but yield yourselves unto God, as those that are alive from the dead, and your members as instruments of righteousness unto God." * Professed Christians, if there were no further light given you than that contained in this text, you would be without excuse in suffering yourselves to be controlled by base passion. The word of God is sufficient to enlighten the most beclouded mind, and it can be understood by those who have any wish to understand it. But in order to give men and women every possible warning, God has sent plain, direct testimonies, pointing them to the word they have neglected to follow. Yet the light is often rejected. Those who serve their own lusts, continue to take pleasure in unrighteousness, notwithstanding the vengeance threatened against those who do such things.

Some will acknowledge the evil of sinful indulgence, yet will excuse themselves by saying that they cannot overcome their passions. This is a terrible admission for a Christian to make. "Let every one that nameth the name of Christ depart from iniquity." † Why is this weakness? — It is because men and women have so long pampered their depraved appetites that they have no power of self-government; — because the lower passions of their nature have taken the reins, and high moral principle, which should be the governing power, is gone. Sensuality has quenched the desire for holiness, and has withered spirituality. The soul is held in lowest bondage.

The sacred covenant of marriage is often made to cover sins of the darkest hue. Men and women professing godliness give way to corrupt passions, and thus place themselves on a level with the brute creation. The powers which God has given them to be preserved in sanctifica-

* Rom. 6 : 12, 13.   † 2 Tim. 2 : 19.

tion and honor, they abuse, yet think they commit no evil. Health and life are sacrificed upon the altar of lust. The higher, nobler powers are brought into subjection to the sensual nature. Those who thus sin may not foresee the result of their course. Could they realize the amount of suffering which they are bringing upon themselves and their children, they would be alarmed, and some, at least, would shun a course which brings such dreadful results. So miserable an existence is entailed upon a large class that death would be to them preferable to life ; and many do die prematurely, their lives ingloriously sacrificed to the basest passions.

By such misuse of the marriage relation, the animal passions are strengthened ; and as these grow stronger the moral and intellectual faculties become weaker. The spiritual is overborne by the sensual. The character thus acquired by the parents is transmitted to the children, and they come into the world with their moral powers weakened and the lower passions predominant. The gross passions of the parents are perpetuated in their children. Satan seeks to lower the standard of purity, and to weaken the self-control of those who enter the marriage relation, because he knows that while the baser passions are in the ascendency, the moral powers grow steadily weaker, and he need have no concern as to their spiritual growth. He knows, too, that in no way can he better stamp his own hateful image upon their offspring, and that he can thus mould their character even more readily than he can the character of the parents.

As I have been shown the dangers of those who profess better things, and the sins that exist among them,— a class who are not suspected of being in any danger from these polluting sins,— I have been led to inquire, "Who, O Lord, shall stand when thou appearest ?" Only those who have clean hands and a pure heart shall abide in the day of his coming. O that I could make all understand their obligation to preserve the body in the best condition to render perfect service to their Maker !

I feel impelled by the Spirit of the Lord to urge my sisters who profess godliness to cherish modesty of deportment and a becoming reserve, "with shamefacedness and sobriety." * The liberties allowed in these corrupt times should be no criterion for Christ's followers. The exhibitions of familiarity which the world tolerates, should not exist among Christians fitting for immortality. If lasciviousness, vice, and crime are the order of the day among those who refuse to be controlled by the principles of God's word, how important that those professing to be followers of Christ, closely allied to God and angels, should show them a better and nobler way ! How important that by their chaste conduct they should stand in marked contrast to the class who are controlled by base passion!

My sisters, avoid even the appearance of evil. In this fast age you are not safe unless you stand on your guard. Virtue and modesty are rare. I appeal to you as followers of Christ, in view of your high profession, to cherish the priceless gem of modesty. As you hope to be finally exalted to join the society of sinless angels, and to live in an atmosphere where there is not the least taint of sin, seek purity ; for nothing else will abide the searching test of the day of God, and be received into a pure and holy heaven.

The slightest insinuation of evil, the least approach to unwarrantable familiarity, from whatever source it may come, should be resented as the worst of insults to your dignified womanhood. If it is from one in high position, who is ministering to the flock of God, the sin is of the greater magnitude, and should lead a God-fearing woman to recoil with horror from the hypocrisy and villainy of one whom the people respect and honor as God's servant. He is handling sacred things, yet hiding his baseness of heart under the cloak of his high calling. Be afraid of anything like this familiarity. Be sure that it is evidence of an impure mind. If you give the least encouragement in this direction, you make it evident that your mind is not pure and chaste as it should be, and that

* 1 Tim. 2 :9.

sin has charms for you. You lower the standard of your womanhood.

Our sisters should cultivate true meekness. They may be courteous ; but they should not be forward, talkative, and bold. To be kind, tender, pitiful, forgiving, and humble is well pleasing to God. If they occupy this position, they will not be burdened with undue attention from the other sex. There will be a sacred circle of purity around them, which will shield them from unwarrantable liberties.

Vainglory, the fashion of the world, the desire of the eye, and the lust of the flesh, are closely connected with the fall of the unfortunate. If these things had been rooted out of the heart, these fallen ones would not be so weak. If women could view these matters as God has presented them to me, they would have such an abhorrence of impurity that they would not be found among those who fall through the temptations of Satan, no matter whom he might select as the medium.

Those godly women whose minds and hearts are occupied in meditating upon themes which strengthen purity of life, and which elevate the soul to commune with God, will not be easily led astray from the path of rectitude and virtue. Such will be fortified against the sophistry of Satan ; they will be prepared to withstand his seductive arts.

My soul mourns for the youth who are forming character in this degenerate age. I tremble for their parents also ; for they do not realize their obligation to train up their children in the way they should go. Custom and fashion are consulted, and as the children soon learn to be swayed by these, they are easily corrupted ; while their careless and indulgent parents are asleep to the danger which threatens their offspring.

But few of the youth are free from corruption. Impure habits are practiced to an alarming extent, and have done more than any other evil to cause the degeneration of the race. Children who indulge secret vice are often puny and dwarfed. The anxious parents seek a physician, and drugs are administered; but the evil is not removed, for the cause still exists.

The victims of this habit do not love work; and when engaged in it, they complain of fatigue, — they have backache, headache, and what not? Be sure, parents, if simple, well-regulated labor exhausts your children, there is something else that is enervating their system. Do not be hasty to excuse them from physical exercise. Do not lift the burdens they should bear. Overwork is hurtful, but indolence is much more to be dreaded. Do not release them from responsibility, and indulge their complaints. It would be the worst thing you could possibly do for them. It would remove almost the only barrier against Satan's free access to their weakened minds. The weariness attending useful labor lessens the inclination to indulge in vice. Active hands and minds do not find time to heed every temptation which the enemy suggests; but idle hands and brains are all ready for him to control. The mind, when not occupied, is inclined to dwell upon improper things. "Behold, this was the iniquity of thy sister Sodom, pride, fullness of bread, and abundance of idleness was in her and in her daughters."*

Children tend naturally to evil. Unless parents keep their children under firm control, with the fear of God before them, Satan will take possession of their young minds, and corrupt them. As they increase in years, the lustful passions grow with their growth and strengthen with their strength. And they cannot rest until their guilty secret is imparted to those with whom they associate. Curiosity is aroused, and the knowledge of vice is passed from youth to youth, from child to child. until there is scarcely one to be found who is ignorant of it. Why do fathers and mothers act as though a lethargy were upon them? They do not mistrust that Satan is sowing evil seed in their families. They are as blind and reckless in regard to these things as it is possible for them to be. Why do they not awake, and inform themselves upon

* Eze. 16:49.

these subjects? Why do they not try to become intelligent in regard to the laws of life, that they may be prepared to care for their own and their children's bodies in a way to promote physical health?

The power of Satan over the youth of this age is fearful. Unless the minds of our children are firmly balanced by religious principle, their morals will become corrupted by the vicious examples with which they come in contact. The greatest danger of the young is from a lack of self-control. Indulgent parents do not teach their children self-denial. The very food they place before them is such as to irritate the stomach. The excitement thus produced is communicated to the brain, and as a result the passions are roused. It cannot be too often repeated, that whatever is taken into the stomach affects not only the body, but ultimately the mind as well. Gross and stimulating food fevers the blood, excites the nervous system, and too often dulls the moral perceptions, so that reason and conscience are overborne by the sensual impulses. It is difficult, and often well-nigh impossible, for one who is intemperate in diet to exercise patience and self-control. Hence the special importance of allowing children, whose characters are yet unformed, to have only such food as is healthful and unstimulating. It was in love that our heavenly Father sent the light of health reform, to guard against the evils that result from unrestrained indulgence of appetite.

"Whether therefore ye eat, or drink, or whatsoever ye do, do all to the glory of God."* Are parents doing this when they prepare food for the table and call the family to partake of it? Do they place before their children that only which they know will make the very best blood, that which will keep the system in the least feverish condition, and will place it in the best relation to life and health? Or do they, regardless of the future good of their children, provide for them unhealthful, stimulating, irritating food?

There is nothing which more surely leads to evil than

to lift all burdens from children, leaving them to an idle, aimless life, to do nothing, or to occupy themselves as they please. The minds of children are active, and if not occupied with that which is good and useful, they will inevitably turn to what is bad. While it is right and necessary for them to have recreation, they should be taught to work, to have regular hours for physical labor, and also for reading and study. See that they have employment suited to their years, and are supplied with useful and interesting books. Satan improves the opportunity to educate idle minds. It is a sin to let children grow up in idleness. Let them exercise their limbs and muscles, even if it wearies them. If they are not overworked, how can weariness harm them more than it harms you ? There is quite a difference between weariness and exhaustion. Children need more frequent change of employment and intervals of rest than grown persons do ; but even when quite young, they may begin learning to work, and they will be happy in the thought that they are making themselves useful. Their sleep will be sweet after healthful labor, and they will be refreshed for the next day's work.

Some do not realize the sinfulness of impure habits, and the sure results. Long indulgence in evil has blinded their understanding. The sensitive nerves of the brain have lost their healthy tone, and the result is a deadening of the moral sensibilities. The solemn message from heaven cannot forcibly impress the heart. Moral power is exceedingly weak when it comes in conflict with established habits. Impure thoughts have control of the imagination, and temptation is almost irresistible. If the mind were accustomed to contemplate elevating subjects, the imagination trained to behold pure and holy things, it would be fortified against temptation. It would linger upon the heavenly, the pure, the sacred, and could not be attracted to the base, corrupt, and vile.

I have some knowledge of Satan's manner of working, and know how well he succeeds in it. He has caused a

paralysis to come upon the minds of parents, and they
are slow to suspect evil habits in their children. Some of
these youth profess to be Christians, and the parents sleep
on, fearing no danger, while their children are wrecking
both body and mind.

It is the special work of Satan in these last days to
take possession of the minds of youth, to corrupt the
thoughts, and inflame the passions; for he knows that by
so doing he can lead to impure actions, and thus all the
noble faculties of the mind will become debased, and he
can control them to suit his own purposes. All are free
moral agents, and as such they must train their thoughts
to run in the right channel. The first work of those
who would reform is to purify the imagination. Our
meditations should be such as will elevate the mind.
"Whatsoever things are true, whatsoever things are honest, whatsoever things are just, whatsoever things are
pure, whatsoever things are lovely, whatsoever things are
of good report; if there be any virtue, and if there be
any praise, think on these things."* Here is a wide field
in which the mind can safely range. If Satan seeks to
turn it to low and sensual things, bring it back. When
corrupt imaginings seek to gain possession of your mind,
flee to the throne of grace, and pray for strength from
heaven. By the grace of Christ it is possible for us to
reject impure thoughts. Jesus will attract the mind, purify the thoughts, and cleanse the heart from every secret
sin. "The weapons of our warfare are not carnal, but
mighty through God; . . . casting down imaginations,
and every high thing that exalteth itself against the
knowledge of God, and bringing into captivity every
thought to the obedience of Christ." †

The youth are seldom taught self-denial and self-control.
They are allowed to have their own way till they become
headstrong and self-willed, and parents are put to their
wit's end to know what course to pursue in order to save
them from ruin. The corrupting doctrine that has prevailed,
that, from a health standpoint, the sexes should mingle

* Phil. 4:8.   † 2 Cor. 10:4, 5.

together, has done its mischievous work. When parents and guardians manifest a tithe of the shrewdness that Satan exercises, then can the association of the sexes be more nearly harmless. As it is, he is only too successful in his efforts to bewitch the minds of the youth, and the association of boys and girls only increases the evil. Young boys have scarcely entered their teens before they begin to show attention to girls of their own age, and the girls show a painful lack of maidenly reserve and modesty.

What is the effect of this association? Does it tend to promote purity? — No, indeed. Children become infatuated with a love-sick sentimentalism, and religion has no influence over them to arrest their wrong course. What can be done to stay the tide of evil? Parents can do much if they will.

If a young girl is accosted with low familiarity, she should be taught to so resent it that no such advances will ever be repeated. When a girl's company is frequently sought by boys or young men, something is wrong. She needs the restraining and guiding influence of a firm and wise mother.

Young persons who are thrown into one another's society, may make their association a blessing or a curse. They may edify and strengthen one another, improving in deportment, in disposition, in knowledge; or, by permitting themselves to become careless and unfaithful, they may exert only a demoralizing influence.

Many of the young are eager for books. They read everything they can obtain. Exciting love stories and the specimens of nude art displayed in art galleries, have a corrupting influence. The imagination becomes defiled. Then follow sins and crimes which drag beings formed in the image of God down below the level of the brutes, and sink them at last in perdition. Avoid reading and seeing things which will suggest impure thoughts. Cultivate a love for high moral and intellectual themes. Let not the noble powers of the mind become enfeebled and perverted by much reading of even story-books. I know of strong minds that have been unbalanced and almost paralyzed, by intemperate and indiscriminate reading.

It requires skill and patient effort to mould the young in the right manner. Especially do children who have come into the world burdened with a heritage of evil, the direct result of the sins of their parents, need the most careful culture to develop and strengthen their moral and intellectual faculties. And the responsibility of the parents is heavy indeed. Evil tendencies are to be carefully restrained and tenderly rebuked ; the mind is to be stimulated in favor of the right. The child should be encouraged in attempting to govern himself. And all this is to be done judiciously, or the purpose desired will be frustrated.

Parents may well inquire, "Who is sufficient for these things?" God alone is their sufficiency ; and if they do not seek his aid and counsel, hopeless indeed is their task. But by prayer, by the study of the Bible, and by earnest zeal on their part, they may succeed nobly in this important duty, and be repaid a hundred-fold for all their time and care. Gossiping and anxiety concerning the external appearance have often taken the precious time that should have been devoted to prayer for wisdom and strength from God to fulfill this most sacred trust. Fathers and mothers who are wise unto salvation will seek to make their surroundings such that they will be favorable to the formation of correct character in their children. The source of wisdom is open to them, and from it they may draw the knowledge which they need. The Bible, a volume rich in instruction, should be their text-book. If they train their children according to its precepts, they are not only setting their young feet in the right path, but are educating themselves in their holy duties as well.

The young should not be suffered to learn good and evil indiscriminately, with the idea that at some future time the good will predominate and the evil lose its influence. The evil will increase faster than the good. It is possible that after many years the evil they have learned may be eradicated ; but who will venture this ? Time is short. It is easier and much safer to sow clean, good seed in the hearts of your children, than to pluck up the weeds afterward. Impressions made upon the minds of the young are hard to efface. How important, then, that these impressions be of the right sort, — that the elastic faculties of youth be bent in the right direction !

Throw around your children the charms of home and of your society. Treat them with candor, Christian tenderness, and love. This will give you a strong influence over them, and they will feel that they can repose unlimited confidence in you. Then they will not have so much desire for the society of young associates. Because of the evils now in the world, and the restriction which it is necessary to place upon children, parents should have double care to bind them to their hearts, and to let them see that they wish to make them happy.

Among the youth there is an inclination to associate with those who are inferior in mind and morals. What real enjoyment can a young person expect from a voluntary association with those who have a low standard of thought, feeling, and deportment ? Some are debased in taste and depraved in habit, and all who choose such companions will be in danger of following their pernicious example.

Those who desire immortality must not allow an impure thought or act. If Christ be the theme of contemplation, the thoughts will be widely separated from every subject which will lead to impurity in action. The mind will be strengthened by dwelling upon elevating subjects. If trained to run in the channel of purity and holiness, it will become healthy and vigorous. If trained to dwell upon spiritual themes, it will come naturally to take that channel. But this attraction of the thoughts to heavenly things cannot be gained without the exercise of faith in God, and an earnest, humble reliance upon him for that strength and grace which will be sufficient for every emergency.

Ample provision has been made for all who sincerely, earnestly, and thoughtfully set about the work of perfecting holiness in the fear of God. Strength and grace have been provided through Christ, to be brought by ministering angels to the heirs of salvation. None are so low, so currupt and vile, that they cannot find in Jesus, who died for them, strength and purity and righteousness, if they will put away their sins, turn from their course of iniquity, and with full purpose of heart seek the living God. He is waiting to take away their stained garments, polluted by sin, and to put upon them the pure robe of his righteousness, to bid them live and not die. In him, as branches of the Living Vine, they may flourish. Their boughs will not wither nor be fruitless. If they abide in him, they can draw nourishment from him, be imbued with his spirit, walk as he walked, overcome as he overcame, and be exalted to his own right hand.

CLEANLINESS AN AID TO PURITY.

"WHY take ye thought for raiment?" "Is not the life more than meat, and the body than raiment?"*

The mother should not give her time and strength to the needless ornamentation of her children's clothing; indeed, she cannot do this if she has a true sense of her accountability to God. It is not essential to trim and embroider clothing; the time thus spent is precious, and should be given to the forming of character, the development of the mind, the inculcation of right principles, to teaching the children purity, modesty, and truthfulness.

Food should be so simple that its preparation will not absorb all the time of the mother. It is true, care should be taken to furnish the table with healthful food prepared in a wholesome and inviting manner. Do not think that anything you can carelessly throw together to serve as food is good enough for the children. But less time should be devoted to the preparation of unhealthful dishes for the table, to please a perverted taste, and more time to the education and training of the children. Let the strength which is now given to the unnecessary planning of what you shall eat and drink, and wherewithal you shall be clothed, be directed to keeping their persons clean and their clothes neat. Do not misunderstand me in this. I do not say that you must keep them in-doors, like dolls. There is nothing impure in clean sand and dry earth; it is the emanations from the body that defile, requiring the clothing to be changed and the body washed.

Frequent bathing is very beneficial, especially at night, just before retiring, or upon rising in the morning. It will take but a few moments to give the children a bath, and to rub them until their bodies are in a glow. This brings the blood to the surface, relieving the brain; and

* Matt. 6:28, 25. (141)

there will be less inclination to indulge in impure practices. Teach the little ones that God is not pleased to see them with unclean bodies and untidy, torn garments. Tell them that he wants them to be pure without and within, that he may dwell with them.

Having the clothing neat and clean will be one means of keeping the thoughts pure and sweet. Every article of dress should be plain and simple, without unnecessary adornment, so that it will be but little work to wash and iron it. Especially should every article which comes in contact with the skin be kept clean, and free from any offensive odor. Nothing of an irritating character should touch the bodies of children, nor should their clothing be allowed to bind them in any way. If more attention were given to this subject, far less impurity would be practiced.

I have often seen children's beds in such a condition that the foul, poisonous odor constantly rising from them was to me unendurable. Keep everything the eyes of the children rest upon and that comes in contact with the body, night or day, clean and wholesome. This will be one means of educating them to choose the cleanly and the pure.

Let the sleeping-room of your children be neat, however destitute it may be of expensive furniture. Begin early to teach the little ones to take care of their clothing. Let them have a place to lay their things away, and be taught to fold every article neatly and put it in its place. If you cannot afford even a cheap bureau, use a dry-goods box, fitting it with shelves, and covering it with some bright, pretty figured cloth. This work of teaching neatness and order will take a little time each day, but it will pay in the future of your children, and in the end will save you much time and care.

If parents desire their children to be pure, they must surround them with pure associations, such as God can approve. The home must be kept pure and clean. Unclean, neglected corners in the house will tend to make impure, neglected corners in the soul. Mothers, you are the educators of your children, and you can do a great deal if you begin early to inculcate pure thoughts, by fitting up their rooms in a cleanly, tasteful, attractive manner. If the children have a room which they know is their own, and if they are taught how to keep it tidy and make it pleasant, they will have a sense of ownership,—they will feel that they have within the home a home of their own, and will have a satisfaction in keeping it neat and nice. The mother will necessarily have to inspect their work, and make suggestions and give instruction. This is the mother's work, and nothing should be permitted to come between her and her children.

When visitors come, as they frequently will, they should not be allowed to absorb all the time and attention of the mother; her children's temporal and spiritual welfare should come first. Time should not be used in preparing rich cakes, pies, and unhealthful viands for the table. These are an extra expense, and many cannot afford it. But the greater evil is in the example. Let the simplicity of the family be preserved. Do not try to give the impression that you can sustain a style of living which is really beyond your means. Do not try to appear what you are not, either in your table preparations or in your manners. While you should treat your visitors kindly, and make them feel at home, you should ever remember that you are a teacher to the little ones God has given you. They are watching you, and no course of yours should direct their feet in a wrong way. Be to your visitors just what you are to your family every day,—pleasant, considerate, and courteous. In this way all can be educators, an example of good works. They testify that there is something more essential than to keep the mind on what they shall eat and drink, and wherewithal they shall be clothed.

Let the mother's dress, also, be simple and neat. So may she preserve her dignity and influence. If mothers allow themselves to wear untidy garments at home, they are teaching their children to follow in the same slovenly way. Many mothers think that anything is good enough for home wear, be it ever so soiled and shabby. But they soon lose their influence in the family. The children draw comparisons between their mother's dress and that of others who dress neatly, and their respect for her is weakened. Mothers, make yourselves as attractive as possible, not by elaborate trimming, but by wearing clean, well-fitting garments. Thus you will give to your children constant lessons in neatness and purity. The love and respect of her children should be of the highest value to every mother. Everything upon her person should teach cleanliness and order, and should be associated in their minds with purity. There is a sense of fitness, an idea of the appropriateness of things, in the minds of even very young children; and how can they be impressed with the desirability of purity and holiness when their eyes daily rest on untidy dresses and disorderly rooms? How can the heavenly guests, whose home is where all is pure and holy, be invited into such a dwelling?

The word of God declares, "Know ye not that your body is the temple of the Holy Ghost, which is in you, which ye have of God, and ye are not your own? For ye are bought with a price; therefore glorify God in your body, and in your spirit, which are God's." *

Parents are under obligation to God to make their surroundings such as will correspond to the truth they profess. They can then give correct lessons to their children, and the children will learn to associate the home below with the home above. The family here must, as far as possible, be a model of the one in heaven. Then temptations to indulge in what is low and groveling will lose much of their force. Children should be taught that they are only probationers here, and educated to become inhabitants of the mansions which Christ is preparing for those who love him and keep his commandments. This is the highest duty which parents have to perform.

* 1 Cor. 6 : 19, 20.

Parents should in a special sense regard themselves as agents of God to instruct their children, as did Abraham, to keep the way of the Lord. They need to search the Scriptures diligently, to know what is the way of the Lord, that they may teach it to their household. Micah says, "What doth the Lord require of thee, but to do justly, and to love mercy, and to walk humbly with thy God?" * In order to be teachers, parents must be learners, gathering light constantly from the oracles of God, and by precept and example bringing this precious light into the education of their children. Teach them that principle should govern their eating, their drinking, and their dressing. Teach them from their very babyhood that God's law is the rule of the house, and that it must be obeyed in all the relations of life; that a disregard of moral law will exist wherever there is a willful disregard of physical law.

The Christian life is one of constant self-denial and self-control. These are the lessons to be taught to the children from their infancy. Teach them that they must practice temperance, purity in thought and heart and act; that they belong to God, because they have been bought with a price, even the precious blood of his dear Son.

* Micah 6 : 8.

HOPE FOR THE TEMPTED.

In order to reach excellency of character, we must realize the value which Christ has placed upon the human race. In the beginning, man was invested with dignity; but he fell through indulgence of appetite. Notwithstanding the great gulf thus opened between God and man, Christ loved the hopeless sinner, and came to our world to bridge the gulf, and unite divine power to human weakness, that in his strength and grace man might wrestle for himself against Satan's temptations, overcome for himself, and stand in his God-given manhood, a victor over perverted appetite and degrading passions. The last words of David to Solomon, then a young man and soon to be honored with the throne of Israel, were, "Be thou strong, . . . and show thyself a man."* To the weak and tempted one I address the same, "Show thyself a man." I point you to the cross of Calvary. I bid you in the name of Jesus, Look and live. Destroy not yourself. With God's blessing it is possible for you to gain the ascendency over appetite and debasing passion.

God has made man capable of constant progress in everything that constitutes mental and moral dignity. No other creature of his hand is capable of such advancement. Man can reach an eminence in self-control and dignity that will raise him above the slavery of appetite and passion, where he can stand before God as a man, his name written in the books of heaven.

Let the light of truth shine into the mind of a man, let the love of God be shed abroad in his heart, and we can hardly conceive what he may be or what God can do through him. Though a fallen son of Adam, he may, through the merits of Christ, be an heir of immortality, his thoughts elevated and ennobled, his heart purified, and his conversation in heaven. Think, O, think of the

*1 Kings 2:2.

superiority of an intelligent Christian man over a poor votary of sin! Note the difference between man blinded by sin, the victim of his own evil passions, and sunk in vice, and a man reclaimed by the truth of God's word, ennobled by looking to Jesus and believing in him, and becoming a partaker of the divine nature.

Look at the condition of the men who give themselves up to intemperance. Littleness, earthliness, degradation, mark their entire character. This is the result of their evil course. They have been walking in the way of their own heart, and in the sight of their own eyes, and are filled with their own devices. Their wretched homes are a hell, made so by themselves. "Whatsoever a man soweth, that shall he also reap." * Shall these men charm you? Would you sink into ignorance and debasement, and become besotted, like them? Shall the habits and practices of these debased creatures, who bear scarcely a trace of the moral image of God, be your pattern? Is not the picture of their degraded condition enough to make you shun the first step in the same direction? Would you desire to be shut out of heaven with such company?

Let me say to him who is struggling to overcome, God presents before you a strong hope, that you may lay hold on eternal life. Lose no opportunity of becoming a man. When you look at yourself, and realize the strength of temptation, you feel so weak in moral power that you say, "I cannot resist." I tell you, you can resist, you must resist temptation. Although you may have been overcome, although moral debasement may have marked your course, it need not always be thus. Jesus is your helper. In his strength you can overcome the beguiling power of appetite. Summon will-power to your aid.

The will is the governing power in the nature of man. If the will is set right, all the rest of the being will come under its sway. The will is not the taste or the inclination, but it is the choice, the deciding power, the kingly

* Gal. 6 : 7.

power, which works in the children of men unto obedience to God or to disobedience.

You will be in constant peril until you understand the true force of the will. You may believe and promise all things, but your promises and your faith are of no account until you put your will on the right side. If you will fight the fight of faith with your will-power, there is no doubt that you will conquer.

Your part is to put your will on the side of Christ. When you yield your will to his, he immediately takes possession of you, and works in you to will and to do of his good pleasure. Your nature is brought under the control of his Spirit. Even your thoughts are subject to him. If you cannot control your impulses, your emotions, as you may desire, you can control the will, and thus an entire change will be wrought in your life. When you yield up your will to Christ, your life is hid with Christ in God. It is allied to the power which is above all principalities and powers. You have a strength from God that holds you fast to his strength; and a new life, even the life of faith, is possible to you.

You can never be successful in elevating yourself, unless your will is on the side of Christ, co-operating with the Spirit of God. Do not feel that you cannot; but say, "I can, I will." And God has pledged his Holy Spirit to help you in every decided effort.

Every one of us may know that there is a power working with our efforts to overcome. Why will not men lay hold upon the help that has been provided, that they may become elevated and ennobled? Why do they degrade themselves by the indulgence of perverted appetite? Why do they not rise in the strength of Jesus, and be victorious in his name? The very feeblest prayer that we can offer, Jesus will hear. He pities the weakness of every soul. Help for every one has been laid upon Him who is mighty to save. I point you to Jesus Christ, the sinner's Saviour, who alone can give you power to overcome on every point.

Heaven is worth everything to us. We must not run any risk in this matter. We must take no venture here. We must know that our steps are ordered by the Lord. May God help us in the great work of overcoming. He has crowns for those that overcome. He has white robes for the righteous. He has an eternal world of glory for those who seek for glory, honor, and immortality. Every one who enters the city of God will enter it as a conqueror. He will not enter it as a condemned criminal, but as a son of God. And the welcome given to every one who enters there will be, "Come, ye blessed of my Father, inherit the kingdom prepared for you from the foundation of the world." *

Gladly would I speak words that would aid such trembling souls to fasten their grasp by faith upon the mighty Helper, that they might develop a character upon which God will be pleased to look. Heaven may invite them, and present its choicest blessings, and they may have every facility to develop a perfect character; but all will be in vain unless they are willing to help themselves. They must put forth their own God-given powers, or they will sink lower and lower, and be of no account for good, either in time or in eternity.

One who is weakened, and even degraded by sinful indulgence, may become a son of God. It is in his power to be constantly doing good to others, and helping them to overcome temptation; and in so doing he will reap benefit to himself. He may be a bright and shining light in the world, and at last hear the benediction, "Well done, good and faithful servant," from the lips of the King of Glory.

* Matt. 25 : 34.

FRAGMENTS.

HEALTH is a treasure. Of all temporal possessions it is the most precious. Wealth, learning, and honor are dearly purchased at the loss of the vigor of health. None of these can secure happiness, if health is lacking. It is a terrible sin to abuse the health that God has given us; such abuses enfeeble us for life, and make us losers, even if we gain by such means any amount of education.

SATAN'S POWER.— The present enfeebled condition of the human family has been presented before me. Every generation has been growing weaker, and diseases of every form afflict the race. Thousands of poor mortals, with deformed, sickly bodies, shattered nerves, and gloomy minds, are dragging out a miserable existence. Satan's power upon the human family increases. If the Lord were not soon to come and put an end to his cruel work, the earth would ere long be depopulated.

I was shown that Satan's power is especially exercised upon the people of God. Many were presented before me in a doubting, despairing condition. The infirmities of the body affect the mind. A cunning and powerful enemy attends our steps, and employs his strength and skill in trying to turn us out of the right way. Too often it is the case that the people of God are not on the watch, and are therefore ignorant of his devices. He works by means which will best conceal himself from view, and he often gains his object.

APPETITE.— Providence has been leading the people of God out from the extravagant habits of the world, away from the indulgence of appetite and passion, to take their stand upon the platform of self-denial, and temperance in all things. The people whom God is leading will be peculiar. They will not be like the world. If they follow the leadings of God, they will accomplish his purposes, and will yield their will to his will. Christ will dwell in the heart. The temple of God will be holy. Your body, says the apostle, is the temple of the Holy Ghost. God does not require his children to deny themselves to the injury of physical strength. He requires them to obey natural law, in order to preserve physical health. Nature's path is the road he marks out, and it is broad enough for any Christian. With a lavish hand God has provided us with rich and varied bounties for our sustenance and enjoyment. But in order for us to enjoy the natural appetite, which will preserve health and prolong life, he restricts the appetite. He says, Beware! restrain, deny, unnatural appetite. If we create a perverted appetite, we violate the laws of our being, and assume the responsibility of abusing our bodies and of bringing disease upon ourselves.

God has bountifully provided for the sustenance and happiness of all his creatures; if his laws were never violated, if all acted in harmony with the divine will, health, peace, and happiness, instead of misery and continual evil, would be the result.

Some are not impressed with the necessity of eating and drinking to the glory of God. The indulgence of appetite affects them in all the relations of life. It is seen in the family, in the church, in the prayer-meeting, and in the conduct of their children. It is the curse of their lives. It prevents them from understanding the truths for these last days.

I saw that God does not require any one to practice such rigid economy as to weaken or injure the temple of God. There are duties and requirements in his word to humble the church, and cause them to afflict their souls; there is no need of making crosses and manufacturing duties to distress the body, in order to cause humility. All this is outside the word of God.

The time of trouble is just before us, and then stern necessity will require the people of God to deny self, and eat merely enough to sustain life; but God will prepare them for that time. In that fearful hour, their necessity will be God's opportunity to impart strength, and sustain his people. But now God requires them to labor with their hands, the thing that is good, and lay by them in store as he has prospered them, and to do their part in sustaining the cause of truth. This is a duty enjoined upon all who are not especially called to labor in word and doctrine, to devote their time to proclaiming to others the way of life and salvation.

Those who labor with their hands, and those who labor in word and doctrine, must have a care to sustain their physical powers; for Satan and his evil angels are warring against them, seeking to undermine their strength. When they can, they should take rest both in body and mind, and should eat of nourishing food; for they will be obliged to use all the power they have. I saw that it does not glorify God in the least for any of his people to make a time of trouble for themselves. There is a time of trouble just before us, but he will prepare us for that fearful conflict.

———

The indulgence of lustful appetite wars against the soul; it is a constant hinderance to spiritual advancement. Those who yield to these lower impulses, bear an accusing conscience; and when strait truths are presented, they are ready to take offense. They are self-condemned, and think that these subjects have been purposely selected in order to reprove them. They feel grieved and injured, and withdraw themselves from the assemblies of the church. Then the conscience is not so disturbed. Thus they soon lose their interest in the meetings, and their love for the truth. If these will crucify fleshly lusts, the arrows of truth will pass harmlessly by them. But while they indulge lustful appetite, and thus cherish their idols, they make themselves a mark for the shafts of truth; if the truth is spoken at all, it must wound them.

———

Some think they cannot reform, that it would ruin their health to leave off the use of tea, tobacco, and flesh-meats. This is a suggestion of Satan. These hurtful stimulants will surely undermine the constitution, and prepare the system for acute disease; for they impair nature's delicate machinery, and batter down the fortifications she has erected against disease and premature decay.

———

Some feel as though they would like to have some-body tell them how much to eat. This is not as it should be. We are to act from a moral and religious standpoint. We are to be temperate in all things, because an incorruptible crown, a heavenly treasure, is before us.

I wish to say to my brethren and sisters, I would have moral courage to take my position, and govern myself. I would not want to put that on some one else. You eat too much, and then you are sorry; and so you keep thinking of what you eat and drink. Just eat that which is for the best, and go right away, feeling clear in the sight of Heaven, and you need not suffer from remorse of conscience.

———

We do not believe in removing temptation entirely away from either children or grown persons. We all have a warfare before us, and must stand in a position to resist the temptations of Satan.

———

Some have sneered at health reform, and have said it was all unnecessary, that it was an excitement which tended to divert minds from present truth. They have said that matters were carried to extremes. Such do not know what they are talking about. While men and women professing godliness are diseased from the crown of the head to the sole of the feet; while their physical, mental, and moral energies are enfeebled through gratification of depraved appetite and excessive labor, how can they weigh the evidences of truth, and comprehend the requirements of God? If their moral and intellectual faculties are beclouded, they cannot appreciate the value of the atonement or the exalted character of the work of God, nor delight in the study of his word. How can a nervous dyspeptic be ready always to give an answer to every man that asketh him, a reason for the hope that is in him, with meekness and fear? How soon would such a one become confused and agitated, and by his diseased imagination be led to view matters in an altogether wrong light, and by a lack of that meekness and calmness which characterized the life of Christ, be caused to dishonor his profession while contending with unreasonable men?

———

As a people, with all our profession of health reform, we eat too much. Indulgence of appetite is the greatest cause of physical and mental debility, and lies at the foundation of a large share of the feebleness which is apparent everywhere.

———

The controlling power of appetite will prove the ruin of thousands, who, if they had conquered on this point, would have had the moral power to gain the victory over every other temptation. But those who are slaves to appetite will fail of perfecting Christian character. The continual transgression of man for over six thousand years has brought sickness, pain, and death as its fruit. And as we draw near the close of time, Satan's temptations to indulge appetite will be more powerful, and more difficult to resist.

———

There are but few who are roused sufficiently to understand how much their habits of diet affect their health, their character, their usefulness in this world, and their eternal destiny. I saw that it is the duty of those who have received the light from heaven, and have realized the benefit of walking in it, to manifest a greater interest for those who are still suffering for want of knowledge. Sabbath-keepers who are looking for the soon appearing of their Saviour should be the last to manifest a lack of interest in this great work of reform. Men and women must be instructed, and ministers and people should feel that the burden of the work rests upon them to agitate the subject and seek to educate others.

To become intelligent upon the subject of hygiene is the duty of every family professing to believe present truth.

Appetite and passion are overcoming thousands of Christ's professed followers. Through familiarity with sin, their senses become so blunted that evil seems attractive to them, rather than abhorrent. The end of all things is at hand. God will not much longer bear with the crimes and debasing iniquity of the children of men. Their sins have reached unto heaven, and will soon be answered by the fearful plagues of God upon the earth. They will drink the cup of his wrath, unmixed with mercy.

CHURCH TRIALS.— The abuses of the stomach by the gratification of appetite are a fruitful source of most church trials. Those who eat and work intemperately and irrationally, talk and act irrationally. It is not necessary to drink alcoholic liquors in order to be intemperate. The sin of intemperate eating — eating too frequently, too much, and of rich, unwholesome food — destroys the healthy action of the digestive organs, affects the brain, and perverts the judgment, preventing rational, calm, healthy thinking and acting. In order for the people of God to be in an acceptable state with him, where they can glorify him in their bodies and spirits, which are his, they must with interest and zeal deny the gratification of appetite, and exercise temperance in all things. Then they can comprehend the truth in its beauty and clearness, and carry it out in their lives, and by a judicious, straight-forward course give the enemies of our faith no occasion to reproach the cause of truth. God requires all who believe the truth to make special, persevering efforts to place themselves in the best possible condition of bodily health, for a solemn and important work is before us. Health of mind and body is required in this work; it is as essential to a healthy religious experience, to advancement in the Christian life, to progress in holiness, as is the hand or foot to the human body. God requires his people to cleanse themselves "from all filthiness of the flesh and spirit, perfecting holiness in the fear of God." * All who are indifferent, and excuse themselves from this work, waiting for the Lord to do for them what he requires them to do for themselves, will be found wanting when the meek of the earth, who have wrought his judgments, are hid in the day of the Lord's anger.

COOKING.— For want of knowledge and skill in regard to cooking, many a wife and mother daily sets before her family ill-prepared food, which is steadily and surely impairing the digestive organs, and making a poor quality of blood; the result is, frequent attacks of inflammatory disease, and sometimes death. Many a life has been sacrificed by the eating of heavy, sour bread. An instance was related to me, of a hired girl who made a batch of such bread. In order to get rid of it and conceal the matter, she threw it to some very large hogs. Next morning the man of the house found his swine dead; and upon examining the trough he found pieces of this heavy bread. He made inquiries, and the girl acknowledged what she had done. She had not thought of the effect of such bread upon the swine. If sour, heavy bread will kill swine, which can devour rattlesnakes and almost every detestable thing, what effect must it have upon that tender organ, the human stomach?

* 2 Cor. 7 : 1.

It is a religious duty for every Christian girl and woman to learn to make good, sweet, light bread from
unbolted wheat flour. Mothers should take their daughters
into the kitchen with them when very young, and teach
them the art of cooking. The mother cannot expect her
daughters to understand the mysteries of housekeeping
without education. She should instruct them patiently,
lovingly, and make the work as agreeable as she can by
her cheerful countenance and words of approval. If they
fail once, twice, or thrice, censure not. Already discouragement is doing its work, and tempting them to say,
"It is no use; I can't do it." This is not the time for
censure. The will is becoming weakened. It needs the
spur of encouraging, cheerful, hopeful words: "Never
mind the mistakes you have made. You are but a
learner, and must expect to make blunders. Try again.
Put your mind on what you are doing. Be very careful,
and you will certainly succeed."

Many mothers fail to realize the importance of this
branch of knowledge, and rather than have the trouble
and care of instructing their children and bearing with
their failures and errors, they prefer to do all the cooking themselves. And when their daughters make mistakes in their efforts, they send them away with, "It is
no use; you can't do this or that. You perplex and
trouble me more than you help." Thus the first efforts
of the learners are repulsed, and the failure so cools their
interest and ardor to learn that they dread another trial,
and will propose to knit, sew, clean house,—anything but
cook. Here the mother was greatly at fault. She should
have patiently instructed them, that they might, by practice, acquire skill and efficiency.

———

We can have a variety of good, wholesome food, cooked
in a healthful manner, so that it will be palatable to all.
It is of vital importance to know how to cook. Poor
cooking produces disease and bad tempers; the system

becomes deranged, and heavenly things cannot be discerned. There is more religion in good cooking than you have any idea of. When I have been away from home sometimes, I have known that the bread upon the table, as well as most of the other food, would hurt me; but I would be obliged to eat a little in order to sustain life. It is a sin in the sight of Heaven to have such food.

MILK AND SUGAR.—Large quantities of milk and sugar eaten together are injurious. They impart impurities to the system. Animals from which milk is obtained are not always healthy. Could we know that animals were in perfect health, I would recommend that people eat flesh-meats sooner than large quantities of milk and sugar. It would not do the injury that milk and sugar do.

There was a case in Michigan to which I will refer. It was that of a man of fine physical appearance. I had previously conversed with him in regard to his manner of living, and was called to visit him in his sickness. "I do not like the looks of your eyes," I said. He was eating large quantities of sugar, and in answer to my question why he did this, he said that he had left off meat, and did not know anything that would supply its place as well as sugar. His food did not satisfy him. This man was suffering simply because his wife did not know how to cook. She was deficient in this important branch of education; and as the result, the poorly cooked food not being sufficient to sustain the demands of the system, sugar was eaten immoderately, and this brought on a diseased condition of the entire system. I tried to tell them as well as I could how to manage, and soon the sick man began to improve. But he imprudently exercised his strength when not able, ate a small amount not of the right quality, and was taken down again. This time there was no help for him. His system seemed to be a living mass of corruption. He died a victim to poor cooking.

DOMESTIC DUTIES FOR STUDENTS. — However good the advantages of the student may be for gaining a knowledge of books, his character is still unformed if he has not an experience in the practical duties of every-day life.

DRESS. — We as a people do not believe it our duty to go out of the world in order to be out of fashion. If we have a plain, neat, modest, comfortable style of dress, and others choose to adopt it, shall we change our dress in order to be different from them? — No; we should not be singular in our dress for the sake of differing from the world: they would despise us for so doing. Christians are the light of the world, the salt of the earth. Their dress should be neat and modest, their conversation chaste and heavenly, and their deportment blameless.

SHUNNING DUTY. — Those who, having had the light upon the subject of eating and dressing with simplicity, in obedience to moral and physical laws, still turn from the light which points out their duty, will shun duty in other things. By shunning the cross which they would have to take up in order to be in harmony with natural law, they blunt the conscience; and they will, to avoid reproach, violate the ten commandments. There is with some a decided unwillingness to endure the cross and despise the shame.

WOMAN'S RIGHTS. — There are speculations as to woman's rights, and her duty in regard to voting; but many women have had no discipline which would qualify them to understand the bearing of important questions. They have lived a life of fashion and self-gratification. Women who might develop a good intellect, who might perfect a noble character, are mere slaves to custom. They lack breadth of thought and intellectual culture. They can talk understandingly of the latest styles of dress, or of the next party or ball; but they are not prepared to act wisely in political matters. They are mere creatures of circumstance.

EXERCISE.—Air is the free blessing of Heaven; it invigorates the whole system. Deprived of pure air, the body becomes diseased, torpid, and enfeebled.

Physicians often advise invalids to visit foreign countries, to go to some mineral spring, or to traverse the ocean, in order to regain health; when, in nine cases out of ten, if they would eat temperately, and engage in healthful exercise with a cheerful spirit, they would regain health, and save time and money. Exercise, and a free, abundant use of the air and sunlight,—blessings which Heaven has bestowed upon all,—would in many cases give life and strength to the emaciated invalid.

Many have suffered from severe mental taxation, unrelieved by physical exercise. The result is a deterioration of their powers, and they are inclined to shun responsibilities. What they need is more active labor. This condition is not confined to those whose heads are white with the frost of time; men young in years have fallen into the same state, and have become mentally feeble.

Strictly temperate habits, combined with exercise of the muscles as well as of the mind, will preserve both mental and physical vigor, and give power of endurance to those engaged in the ministry, to editors, and to all others whose habits are sedentary.

Ministers, teachers, and students do not become as intelligent as they should in regard to the necessity of physical exercise in the open air. They neglect this duty, a duty which is most essential to the preservation of health. They closely apply their minds to study, and yet eat the allowance of a laboring man. Under such habits, some grow corpulent, because the system is clogged. Others become thin and feeble, because their vital powers are exhausted in throwing off the excess of food. The liver is burdened, being unable to throw off the impurities of the blood, and sickness is the result. If physical exercise were combined with mental exertion, the circulation of the blood would be quickened, the action of the heart would be more perfect, impure matter would be thrown off, and new life and vigor would be felt in every part of the body.

When the minds of ministers, school teachers, and students are continually excited by study, and the body is allowed to be inactive, the nerves of emotion are taxed, while the nerves of motion are inactive. The wear being wholly on the mental organs, they become overworked and enfeebled, while the muscles lose their vigor for want of employment. There is no inclination to exercise the muscles in physical labor; exertion seems to be irksome.

It is a sacred work in which we are engaged. The apostle Paul exhorts his brethren, "Having therefore these promises, dearly beloved, let us cleanse ourselves from all filthiness of the flesh and spirit, perfecting holiness in the fear of God." * It is a duty that we owe to God to keep the spirit pure, as a temple for the Holy Ghost. If the heart and mind are devoted to the service of God, obeying all his commandments, loving him with all the heart, might, mind, and strength, and our neighbor as ourselves, we shall be found loyal and true to the requirements of Heaven.

We are now in God's workshop. Many of us are rough stones from the quarry. But as the truth of God is brought to bear upon us, every imperfection is removed, and we are prepared to shine as lively stones in the heavenly temple, where we shall be brought into association, not only with the holy angels, but with the King of heaven himself.

* 2 Cor. 7 : 1.

The consciousness of right-doing is the best medicine for diseased bodies and minds. The special blessing of God resting upon the receiver is health and strength. A person whose mind is quiet and satisfied in God, is in the pathway to health. To have a consciousness that the eyes of the Lord are upon us, that his ears are open to our prayers, is a satisfaction indeed. To know that we have a never-failing Friend to whom we can confide all the secrets of the soul, is a privilege which words can never express. Those whose moral faculties are beclouded by disease are not the ones rightly to represent the Christian life or the beauties of holiness. They are too often in the fire of fanaticism, or the water of cold indifference or stolid gloom. The words of Christ are of more worth than the opinions of all the physicians in the universe: "Seek ye first the kingdom of God, and his righteousness, and all these things shall be added unto you."*

* Matt. 6 : 33.

BIBLE HYGIENE.

INTRODUCTION.

[HYGIENE from a Bible standpoint has always been a favorite theme with Mrs. White. Her husband, Elder James White, was also especially interested in the study of Bible hygiene, and took great pleasure in showing the wonderful harmony between true science and the Scriptures. His intimate acquaintance with the views of his wife, and his own experience with disease during several attacks of grave illness, by which he was led to a most careful consideration of the various phases of the health question, qualified him in a peculiar manner to write and speak intelligently upon this subject. The reader will be both interested and instructed by the perusal of the following collation of the more important writings of Elder White on the subject of hygiene from a Bible standpoint.]

The eccentric Lorenzo Dow once truthfully said that prejudice is like a cork in a bottle ; it does not let anything out, neither does it let anything into the bottle. So blind prejudice will blockade the mind, and not allow errors to pass out of it, nor the plainest truths to enter in. It is asking too much when we say to men, "Give up your prejudices." But few could do this, should they try. In fact, they have a right to their prejudices, if held subordinate to reason. Hence we do not ask men to surrender their prejudices ; but we do invite Christians, in the name of reason and religion, to so far waive their prejudices as to weigh evidence in the scales of reason and justice.

With a large portion of the people, the Bible is the highest and safest authority in all matters of truth and duty. Prove to Christian men and women, who fear God and tremble at his word, that existing reformatory movements are in strict harmony with the teachings of the Sacred Scriptures, and they will no longer regard them as unworthy of their notice. But the very general impression that the restrictions of hygienic practice are not sustained by the word of God, has placed many sincere Christians where it is difficult to reach them.

It is a painful fact that vain philosophy, driveling skepticism, and the extremes of some who have been connected with the health reform movement, have done much to prejudice sincere persons against the true philosophy of health. But those who revere God and his holy word can be reached with the plain declarations of Scripture. We hope to make it appear that the Bible does not justify Christians in many of the common and fashionable habits of our time, — habits which sustain a close relation to life and health, — but that it does demand of them changes from these injurious practices. If we succeed in doing this, it will be considered highly proper, by all Bible Christians, that the attention of the Christian public should be called to the subject of Bible Hygiene.

"God is love;" and his revealed will relates to man's well-being in this life, as well as in that which is to come. Our heavenly Father does not take pleasure in the miseries of this mortal state. He delights in the happiness of obedient intelligences in this world, as well as in the rapturous joys of the redeemed in the world to come. The Bible teaches how to so live in this life as to promote that health and happiness so favorable to the securing of eternal life. True godliness does not blindly overlook and stupidly neglect the laws of our present existence, and try to view (however dimly) the immortal state only. Godliness is profitable unto all things. It gives promise of the life that now is, and also of that which is to come.

The religion of the Bible was not intended simply as a garment to cover moral and physical impurities. It was designed to convert the entire man, — soul, body, and spirit, — that he might be pure without and within. That bogus piety which would give license to consecrated gluttony, devoted lust, and sanctified filthiness, is simply a burlesque upon the religion of the Bible. "Wherefore come out from among them, and be ye separate, saith the Lord, and touch not the unclean ; and I will receive you, and will be a Father unto you, and ye shall be my sons and daughters, saith the Lord Almighty. Having therefore these promises, dearly beloved, let us cleanse ourselves from all filthiness of the flesh and spirit, perfecting holiness in the fear of God."* This is Bible religion. This is true godliness. It proposes to elevate in this life, make fallen beings real men, pure without and within here, and glorified saints in the world to come.

The record of man's creation, the ample provisions made for his comfort, his glorious surroundings, — all these attest the love of God to created intelligences in this life. "And the Lord God formed man of the dust of the ground, and breathed into his nostrils the breath of life ; and man became a living soul. And the Lord God planted a garden eastward in Eden ; and there he put the man whom he had formed. And out of the ground made the Lord God to grow every tree that is pleasant to the sight, and good for food." †

Of all the creatures that God made, man was his best work. He was formed in the image of his Creator, and was made lord over the Creator's works. Physically considered, Adam must have been a noble being. "God saw everything that he had made, and, behold, it was very good." ‡ In its highest sense, this was true of the first man, both intellectually and physically. From Adam to the flood the patriarchs each lived nearly a thousand years. And may we not suppose that the race has fallen off in size and physical strength, in proportion to the average length of life then and now ? Noah lived nine hundred and fifty years. For a time he and his sons

*2 Cor. 6 : 17, 18 ; 7 : 1.   †Gen. 2 : 7-9.   ‡Gen. 1 : 31.

must of necessity have eaten flesh as food, and from that point of time the race rapidly declined in length of days. The original curse, with all its accumulated weight of transgression and violation of natural law, has bowed down the race, and caused man to dwindle to his present brief period of existence, marked with disease, decrepitude, and imbecility.

With this view of the subject, we see Adam in Eden, standing in the glory of his manhood, a grand specimen of the perfect work of God. Earth has long since forgotten the grandeur, the beauty, the perfect symmetry, which characterized the first man before there fell upon him the blight of the curse. And there is so close a connection between matter and mind, that when we consider him intellectually, we are carried up in contemplation of what an intellect might have been, unaffected by the extremes incident to the curse and the depraving and depressing influence of continued transgression, until we are well-nigh lost in conjecture. We behold happy Adam, in holy Eden, walking and talking with God, the great originator of thought, and communing face to face with his Son and with the holy angels, the companion of the highest order of intelligences.

Has man been progressing for six thousand years?— Verily, downward, *downward!* We have only to look back to our parents as they were in the strength of their noon of life, and to our grandparents as their still nobler frames were bowed with the weight of years, to be impressed with the fact that each successive generation suffers under greater physical feebleness than the one before it. This is especially true of American women. It has finally come to this, that by reason of artificial habits and in-door life, and the feebleness thus engendered, not one woman in ten, in our country, is capable of bearing well-developed offspring.

And while we admit that, in the providence of God, the present is an age of discovery and invention,—and many of these things are a necessity to the very existence of this enfeebled generation, — we cannot but regard the popular idea of the increase of mental strength as at war with sound philosophy and the facts in the case.

"But what will you do with the text," says some old fogy, who has for a quarter of a century been dreaming of the golden age of mental progression, "that declares that every generation grows weaker and wiser?" We reply that the Sacred Scriptures contain no such text. This saying can be found only among those maxims that are about one half true and the other half false. Facts compel us to admit the weakness of the present generation, and seriously to question its superior wisdom. Those who have listened to the words of the eloquent Wendell Phillips, in his lecture upon the Lost Arts, must have been impressed with the fact that wisdom has not been especially reserved for the present generation.

"A sound mind in a sound body," is a maxim worthy of a place in the writings of Moses, Solomon, or Paul. Natural and correct habits of life result in health, physical force, mental clearness, and mental strength. Artificial and incorrect habits always tend to physical and mental enfeeblement. We call in question the sanity of those writers who blow hot and cold, in first representing that the bad habits of the present generation are ruinous to body and soul, to physical, mental, and moral strength ; and then, by way of change in the exercises, strike up the popular siren song of grand progression !

But we turn from the sad picture of degeneracy to contemplate again the first man. God in love created him to enjoy the delights of taste, and to feast the eye on the beautiful. To this end his senses were perfect. "And out of the ground made the Lord God to grow every tree that is pleasant to the sight, and good for food." The God of the Bible is the author of all that is really beautiful ; and we please him best when we, within proper limits, love that which he has made lovely. The great God has prepared a feast for the sight, as well as for the taste. We should provide for the proper gratification of both. The thousands who build large pig-pens and extensive hen-parks, and yet grumble over the labor and expense required to produce the sweet adornments of flowers, shrubs, and ornamental trees, are hardly within speaking distance of the Christian's beautiful heaven. But, thank God, we may not only feast the eye with the beauties of nature, but by returning to more natural habits of eating and drinking, we may educate and restore the appetite so as to enjoy much of the original delights of taste.

Contemplating the good things which God has made for the happiness of men, and the present enjoyment which they may afford a sanctified sight and taste, we look back over six thousand years of transgression of divine and natural law, — during which time the curse has been rending the earth, man has been degenerating, and moral darkness, like the pall of death, has enveloped groaning creation, — and exclaim, What must have been the delights of Eden before sin entered !

FOOD, AIR, AND EXERCISE.

THE Bible was given for the well-being of man in this life, as well as a rule by which he may attain to immortal life. And the first grand hygienic rule laid down was that which prescribed man's diet. God said to Adam, "Behold, I have given you every herb bearing seed, which is upon the face of all the earth, and every tree, in the which is the fruit of a tree yielding seed; to you it shall be for meat."* To every tree of the garden, excepting one, our first parents were to have free access.†

The very general belief that the Bible sustains flesh-eating, swine's flesh not excepted, makes it difficult to impress the minds of Christian men and women with the importance of adopting the vegetarian diet, until this false notion is removed. We are aware, however, that it is no small task to remove prejudice from minds, especially on subjects in which appetite is concerned.

There are certain facts which have an important bearing upon the subject of flesh as an article of food. These we will briefly notice.

It was not the plan of God in creation that the life of any of his creatures should be taken. Death, in man or beast, wherever it might exist, came in consequence of sin, and this whole mammoth custom of taking the life of God's creatures to sustain human life, is simply the fruit of transgression. Had our first parents maintained their Eden innocence, had the curse never fallen upon man or beast, the earth would never have been stained with a drop of blood; the almost universal custom of flesh-eating, with its attendant pain and death, would never have been known.

The Creator, in definitely stating what should constitute food for man, did not mention flesh. If he had formed the human teeth to tear the flesh of animals, as some urge, and designed that we should subsist largely upon animal food, flesh would have been at least mentioned in Adam's bill of fare. The word *meat*, as used in the Bible, means simply food, and is so defined by the best authorities. The American Tract Society's Bible Dictionary says: "*Meat*, in the English Bible, usually signifies food, and not merely flesh. Gen. 1 : 29, 30; Matt. 15 : 37. So in Luke 24 : 41 : 'Have ye here any meat?' literally, anything to eat? The meat-offerings of the Jews were made of flour and oil. Leviticus 2." William Smith, classical examiner of the University of London, in his Dictionary of the Bible, says of the word *meat:* "It does not appear that the word *meat* is used in any one instance in the authorized version of either the Old or the New Testament in the sense which it now almost exclusively bears of animal food. The latter is denoted uniformly by *flesh*." Animal food, then, did not constitute any part of the bill of fare of the holy pair in Eden. As true as the book of Genesis, that first venerable gentleman, who lived nine hundred and thirty years, without either the dyspepsia or the gout, was a vegetarian.

So far as we can learn from the sacred record, it was not until after the flood, a period of more than sixteen hundred years from the expulsion from Eden, that permission was given man to eat flesh. Its use had then become a matter of necessity. The waters of the flood had been upon the earth more than a year. By this time the patriarch's stock of provisions must have been very low, and the desolated earth could furnish nothing until it could be produced from the seed preserved in the ark. In this state of things, God said to Noah, "Every moving thing that liveth shall be meat for you; even as the green herb have I given you all things."* The very language of this permission conveys the idea that, up to that time, the green herb, or that which grew out of the ground, — vegetables, fruits, and grains, — constituted man's diet.

And certainly, judging from the sacred record, that

* Gen. 9 : 3.

was a time of remarkably good health. From Adam to Noah, a period of more than sixteen hundred years of vegetarian living, no mention is made of the sickness and death of children, of feebleness in youth or middle age, or of fevers, dyspepsia, gout, or consumption. All lived in the full enjoyment of health nearly one thousand years, or until the springs of life, at last grown weary, stood still. Obituary notices of that time do not mention local diseases, which in our day are caused by the breaking down of certain organs of the system while others remain strong. We read of no sufferings long drawn out, no excruciating agonies in death. The record simply gives the measure of each life, and its cessation.

"And all the days that Adam lived were nine hundred and thirty years; and he died."

"And all the days of Seth were nine hundred and twelve years; and he died."

"And all the days of Enos were nine hundred and five years; and he died."

"And all the days of Cainan were nine hundred and ten years; and he died."

"And all the days of Mahalaleel were eight hundred ninety and five years; and he died."

"And all the days of Jared were nine hundred sixty and two years; and he died."

"And all the days of Methuselah were nine hundred sixty and nine years; and he died."

"And all the days of Lamech were seven hundred seventy and seven years; and he died." *

As the second hygienic principle in the ample provision for man's happy existence, we notice the natural beauties with which the Creator surrounded him. "And out of the ground made the Lord God to grow every tree that is pleasant to the sight." † If after the three-fold curse on account of sin — first, that which followed the sin of Adam; second, that which followed the first murder; and, third, the terrible curse of the flood, which left a large portion of the earth's surface in its present

* See Genesis 5.   † Gen. 2 : 9.

broken and barren condition — if after six thousand years of the blighting, dwindling, deforming influence of the curse, there remains real beauty in the trees, vines, shrubs, and flowers, — a beauty more exquisite than can be found in the finest works of art, — what must have been the grandeur and glory of the trees and flowers of Paradise, fresh from the hand of the Infinite Artist!

And the Son of God, in addressing the "innumerable multitude," pointed them to the delicate lily, declaring that "Solomon in all his glory was not arrayed like one of these." * The superiority of the works of nature over those of art, was not a matter of debate with the Son of God. A single lily in his day, from the soil which had long felt the blight and mildew of the curse, possessed more glory than Solomon in all his royal array. If this be true of a single lily of the field four thousand years from the original glory of creation, what must have been the delights of our first parents as they stood in Eden before sin had paralyzed their senses, or the curse had touched a single leaf!

Man's employment, as seen in the original design, is also worthy of notice. "The Lord God took the man, and put him into the garden of Eden to dress it and to keep it." † Man was designed for activity in the open light of the sun and the free air of heaven. These conditions were important to the joys of his existence. The subsequent curse upon Adam was not in that he should labor, but that his labors should be attended with difficulties. ‡

The natural habits of the people for the first generations after the fall were evidently conducive to longevity and health. There is no mention of houses until the flood. Before that event, and long after it, many of the people, at least, dwelt in tents. Hiding away from sunlight and pure air, behind closed doors, together with other artificial habits, has well-nigh ruined the race. None but those worthy of death, or the next thing to it — close confinement in prison — should be made to suffer such wretched

---

* Matt. 6 : 29. † Gen. 2 : 15. ‡ Gen. 3 : 17–19.

treatment. We admire that simple wisdom which said, "Truly the light is sweet, and a pleasant thing it is for the eyes to behold the sun."*

Proper exercise in the open air and genial sunshine, ranks among God's highest and richest blessings to man. It gives form and strength to the physical organism, and, all other habits being equal, is the surest safeguard against disease and premature decay. Being man's natural condition, it also gives buoyancy and strength to thought, and the mind maintains a healthful balance, free from the extremes resulting from artificial life.

It is true that artificial habits, which are in almost everything wrong, have so far perverted and enfeebled our nature that we are ill-prepared to enter at once upon the natural habits of the worthy patriarchs. We cannot begin where they did. Something may be done, but it is vain to talk of regaining all that has been lost in size, strength, health, and length of days. For this, however, we earnestly plead, that the spirit of reform in habits of life may get hold of the minds of sensible men and women, and that the rapid downward current may be checked.

The tendency to feebleness and premature decay in American women, is too evident to admit of a doubt, and to no one thing is it so clearly traceable as to their habit of staying so closely in-doors. The aboriginal women of our country are as strong as the men. And why? — Simply because their habits are so nearly like those of the men, — spending, as they do, so much of their time in the open air. This is also true, to a large extent, of European women who labor side by side with their husbands in the field.

Every room, and especially every sleeping-room, in the house, should be well-ventilated throughout the year, both by day and by night. The amount of out-door air that should be admitted, must be regulated by its temperature, and by the ability of the inmates to endure. Every man, woman, and child should enjoy as much of God's good

* Eccl. 11 :7.

sunshine as the circumstances will possibly allow. Admit
the light and air, friends, into your houses, and let these
grand medicines, wisely mixed by our gracious God, make
you strong, healthy, and happy.

SWINE'S FLESH.

Among the creatures distinctly pointed out in the Bible
as "unclean," the swine holds a prominent place, yet it
has become a common article of food, even in civilized
and enlightened nations. We speak particularly of the
flesh of this animal because of its nature, and its common
and abundant use by many Christians. These people
profess to receive the word of God as a rule of faith and
practice, and yet that very word says of the swine, "It is
unclean unto you. Ye shall not eat of their flesh, nor
touch their dead carcass."* If it be said that this prohibition is Jewish, and therefore not binding upon Christians,
we reply:—

1. The distinction between the clean beasts and the unclean, recognized at the flood, long before the existence of
a Jew, was established upon the nature and habits of the
creatures which God had made. This distinction received
the sanction of law in the days of Moses; not, however,
because God would have an arbitrary rule for the Jews
during sixteen centuries, but because the forbidden things
were of themselves unclean, and unfit for man to use as food.

2. The nature of the swine is plainly given as the reason
why the Hebrews should not eat of it, nor touch its dead
carcass. "*It is unclean unto you.*" With this agree the
words of the prophet, which class swine's flesh with the
"broth of abominable things." If it be said that these
words were given through Jewish prejudice, then we reply
that it is the great God that speaks. He changes not, and
never speaks from prejudice. Hear him:—

"I have spread out my hands all the day unto a rebell-
ious people, which walketh in a way that was not good,
after their own thoughts; a people that provoketh me to
anger continually to my face; that sacrificeth in gardens,

* Deut. 14:8.

and burneth incense upon altars of brick; which remain among the graves, and lodge in the monuments; which eat swine's flesh, and broth of abominable things is in their vessels." *

"For, behold, the Lord will come with fire, and with his chariots like a whirlwind, to render his anger with fury, and his rebuke with flames of fire. For by fire and by his sword will the Lord plead with all flesh; and the slain of the Lord shall be many. They that sanctify themselves, and purify themselves in the gardens, behind one tree in the midst [*margin*, one after another], eating swine's flesh, and the abomination, and the mouse, shall be consumed together, saith the Lord." †

The candid reader, after a careful examination of the chapters from which we have quoted, will entertain doubts as to their application to the Jewish age. In fact, it is evident that they apply to the present age, and that the last quotation, with its threatened judgment for sins, such as eating swine's flesh, applies definitely to the close of the present age.

Dr. Adam Clarke once said that if he were to offer a burnt-offering to the devil, he should choose a pig stuffed with tobacco. At one time, when invited to ask the blessing at the table, he used these words: "Lord, bless this bread, these vegetables and fruit; and if thou canst bless under the gospel what thou didst curse under the law, bless this swine's flesh."

God said of the flesh of swine in the days of Moses: "It is unclean unto you." What change can have taken place to make it clean, and a proper article of food for Christians? Has God changed his mind on the subject? Has man so changed that what was unclean as an article of food for the Hebrews has become clean to Christians? Or, has the change taken place in the animal? Has the change from the Jewish dispensation improved the nature of hogs? And does the freedom of the world-wide proclamation of the glorious gospel of Jesus Christ give liberty to Christians to eat those things which were an abomination if eaten by the Hebrews?

* Isa. 65 : 2–4.   † Isa. 66 : 15–17.

" But did not God make the swine ? "

We reply that he did, and that he also made dogs, cats, rats, mice, and toads ; not, however, for Christians to eat.

" Then for what were the swine made ? "

We may not fully understand why God made rats, lizards, and rattlesnakes ; but we are very grateful that we are not obliged to eat all the brutes and reptiles which cannot be definitely assigned to other uses.

The influence of swine-eating upon the human system is in some cases terrible almost beyond description. The word *scrofula*, which represents a disease very prevalent in our day, the almost endless varieties of which may be named legion, comes from the Latin word *scrofa*, which signifies " a breeding sow," the mother of abominations. And it may be a question whether the word, or the terrible disease signified by it, would have existed, had man never eaten swine's flesh.

The very nature and disposition of the swine accords with his gross habits and diseased flesh. We do not say that the moral evil of swine-eating is proportionate to the physical ; but we do say that the very close connection between the physical and the mental, between matter and mind, would lead one to conclude that the physical ruin would tend to debase the moral nature.

DIET AND CLEANLINESS OF THE HEBREWS.

IN the record of God's providential dealings with the race, the Hebrews hold a high rank. These descendants of the worthy patriarchs, Abraham, Isaac, and Jacob, were proud of the blood in their veins, and in the days of Christ were heard to say boastfully, "We have Abraham to our father." *

Abraham was a truly grand character. "I know him," says the great God, "that he will command his children and his household after him." † He is called the father of the faithful. The reason his children were to be in number as the dust of the earth, or as the sand upon the sea-shore, or as the stars of heaven, is given thus: "Because that Abraham obeyed my voice, and kept my charge, my commandments, my statutes, and my laws." ‡ The secret of his moral greatness lay in the fact that he was true to principle, and possessed unlimited faith in God, and in his providential dealings with the faithful.

There is much of thrilling interest in the sacred sketches of Isaac, of Jacob and his twelve sons, of the bondage of Joseph and his elevation in Egypt, and of the subsequent slavery of the Hebrews and their miraculous deliverance. God designed to do great things for his people; hence it was his purpose, in his dealings with them, to restrict appetite, and to provide for them the most healthful food.

During centuries of slavery in a heathen land, the habits of the Hebrews had become more or less corrupted. And as their moral powers grew weak, in the same degree, appetite and passion grew strong. With a mighty hand, and with an outstretched arm, God led them from the land of servitude into the wilderness, where he proposed to reform them. Their wrong habits in Egypt

*Matt. 3:9. †Gen. 18:19. ‡Gen. 26:4, 5. (177)

had made them irritable, and had disqualified them to
endure the pangs of thirst, or the gnawings of perverted
appetite.

In their journeying they soon came to Marah. The
water here was bitter, and a cry of murmuring ran
through the host, "What shall we drink?" A certain
tree cast into the waters made them sweet. This quieted
the murmuring of the people for the time. The Lord
"made for them a statute and an ordinance, and there he
proved them, and said, If thou wilt diligently hearken to
the voice of the Lord thy God, and wilt do that which
is right in his sight, and wilt give ear to his commandments, and keep all his statutes, I will put none of these
diseases upon thee, which I have brought upon the Egyp-
tians; for I am the Lord that healeth thee."*

The candid reader will not fail to see that the gracious
God of the Hebrews regarded the health of his people as
a matter of great importance. He promised them health
if they would obey him. Indeed, no fact appears more
distinct in the sacred record than this, that in the great
work of reforming them, and restoring them from wrong
habits contracted in Egypt,—habits which affected the
physical, the moral, and the spiritual nature,—God com-
menced with the appetite.

God did not propose to work miracles for the health of his
people, while they were indulging habits injurious to health.
He was soon to take the Israelites to the land he had
promised them,—a second Eden, marred somewhat by the
curse,—and to establish them there a healthy, happy, holy
people. But before doing this, he would reform them in their
dietetic habits, by taking them back, step by step, as near
as possible to the purity of his original purpose when he
provided the simple fruits, grains, and vegetables as the
best food for man.

Thirty days after the departure from Egypt, the Hebrews were encamped in the wilderness of Sin, and there
the circumstances of their position tested their trembling
faith. It was evident that the chances for food were against

*Ex. 15:24-26.

them, unless God should work a perpetual miracle. And the infidel question was murmured through the camp, "Can God furnish a table in the wilderness?" The whole congregation murmured against Moses and Aaron, saying, "Would to God we had died by the hand of the Lord in the land of Egypt, when we sat by the flesh-pots, and when we did eat bread to the full; for ye have brought us forth into this wilderness, to kill this whole assembly with hunger." *

The case was an urgent one. Something must be done. The people must have food. The necessity of his people was God's opportunity. Food came in abundance from heaven, and lay round about the camp. The God and Father of his people being judge in the case, he most certainly gave them that food which was best adapted to their wants. Well, did he send down to them cattle, sheep, swine, lobsters, oysters, clams, eels, and the like, tea, coffee, and tobacco? This he could, and would, have done, if these were necessary to life and health. But none of these were given. What did the God of Israel provide as food for that vast host? The following simple language gives the answer : —

"Then said the Lord unto Moses, Behold, I will rain bread from heaven for you; and the people shall go out and gather a certain rate every day, that I may prove them, whether they will walk in my law, or no." * God was about to repeat his law in the hearing of all the people. Would they obey? Their appetites and passions were such that their obedience was a matter of doubt. This, however, seems to have been established in the Divine Mind, that unless they could control appetite, they could not be controlled by law. God proposed to prove their moral power, and he did it by testing them on the point of appetite.

From the description of the manna, one might safely conclude that it would be quite as disagreeable to a morbid taste as graham bread. Its shape, color, taste, and the manner in which it was prepared for food, are thus

* Ex. 16: 3, 4.

given : " The manna was as coriander seed, and the color thereof as the color of bdellium.   And the people went about, and gathered it, and ground it in mills, or beat it in a mortar, and baked it in pans, and made cakes of it ; and the taste of it was as the taste of fresh oil." *

It appears from the record that the people were not at first restricted to manna alone.   In the morning they were to eat of the manna, and in the evening they were to eat of the flesh of quails.   Whether flesh was given them once a day at first, that the change of their habits might be more gradual, or because of their frenzied mur-murings, may be a matter of debate.   But at a later period they were restricted to manna alone, as the following statement shows : —

" The mixed multitude that was among them fell a lusting ; and the children of Israel also wept again, and said, Who shall give us flesh to eat ?   We remember the fish which we did eat in Egypt freely ; the cucumbers, and the melons, and the leeks, and the onions, and the garlic ; but now our soul is dried away.   There is nothing at all, besides this manna, before our eyes." *   God gave them flesh, not because it was best for them, but to teach them that he best knew their real needs.   As other means of instruction had failed, he let them have their own way this time, to humble them, and bring them to submission.

The leader of murmuring Israel was instructed to say to the people : " Ye shall eat flesh ; for ye have wept in the ears of the Lord, saying, Who shall give us flesh to eat ? for it was well with us in Egypt ; therefore the Lord will give you flesh, and ye shall eat.   Ye shall not eat one day, nor two days, nor five days, neither ten days, nor twenty days ; but even a whole month, until it come out at your nostrils, and it be loathsome unto you ; because that ye have despised the Lord which is among you, and have wept before him, saying, Why came we forth out of Egypt ? " *

We are sometimes gravely informed by those knowing gentlemen who give their influence on the side of indulg-

<hr />

* Num. 11 : 7, 8, 4-6, 18-20.

ence of morbid taste, that the appetite indicates what is best adapted to the wants of the system. On the same ground, men may justify the drunkard, the opium inebriate, and the tobacco slave. Thousands are acting the glutton, and hastening to a wretched end, over this miserable untruth. How terribly false it was in the case of the Hebrews!

The great God, in his dealings with the Hebrews in the wilderness, not only restricted their diet to the simple manna, but he also taught them cleanliness. Both these restrictions were designed to promote health. Gluttony and filth are base companions; while temperance and cleanliness are congenial friends.

The excellent maxim, "Cleanliness is next to godliness," is not found in the Scriptures, as many suppose, but in the Jewish Talmud. Yet he who reads the books of Moses attentively will not fail to observe that in those moral lessons which were given to the people through Moses, cleanliness holds a high rank among the acts preparatory to acceptance with God.

When the Hebrews were about to assemble at the base of Sinai, to witness the grandeur of Jehovah as he should descend upon the mount, wrapped in a cloud of glory, to speak the ten precepts of his holy law, the following was one of the preparations which the Lord directed Moses to make for the occasion: "Go unto the people, and sanctify them to-day and to-morrow, *and let them wash their clothes.*" * This act of cleanliness, given so specifically in the sacred record, was one of importance. It was not commanded simply because our heavenly Father was pleased to see his children dressed in clean apparel; but it was to impress them with the purity of God, and to show them that he cared for their physical as well as their moral well-being.

While the vast hosts of the Hebrews were in the wilderness, it was necessary for their physical and moral good that they should be neat and cleanly in their common habits. The particulars of the command given them are recorded in Deut. 23 : 10–14.

* Ex. 19 : 10.

That holy God of the Hebrews, who could not view moral or physical impurities with complacency, is the Christian's God. The death of his Son for the sins of men, and the world-wide proclamation of his glorious gospel, were never designed to give the idea that the Christian should be less particular and cleanly in the common habits of life than the Hebrew. Such habits were necessary to physical and moral health, and, from the very nature of the case, the same necessity exists in our time.

It is the most degrading and miserable fanaticism to suppose that the freedom of the gospel consists in slovenly dress, in rough, clownish, irreverent words and actions, or in careless, filthy habits of life. It is painful to state that there is much which passes with certain classes as plain, humble religion, that is a living disgrace to the Christian name. This results from the erroneous idea that God has abolished the rules of cleanliness found in the books of Moses, and that the gospel frees us from their restraint.

God is the same, yesterday, to-day, and forever. The same practical instructions which he gave to the Hebrews through Moses, for their physical and moral benefit, he also impressed upon the minds of the inspired writers of the New Testament. Paul exhorts his readers: "Wherefore come out from among them, and be ye separate, saith the Lord, and touch not the unclean; and I will receive you, and will be a Father unto you, and ye shall be my sons and daughters, saith the Lord Almighty."[*] Acceptance and heirship are the greatest blessings that God can offer on conditional promise to mortal men. Paul continues in the very next verse: "Having therefore these promises, dearly beloved, let us cleanse ourselves from all filthiness of the flesh and spirit, perfecting holiness in the fear of God." In these impressive words the purity (or impurity) of the physical nature is connected with that of the moral nature. The one is dependent upon the other. Filthy habits tend to moral impurity. The man who obtains real purity of spirit, will be led to cleanly habits of

[*] 2 Cor. 6:17, 18.

life. Cleanliness, health, and purity of spirit, are from the same source, and are priceless adornments of the Christian.

God pity the poor! They labor under disadvantages, but they can be cleanly, neat, and orderly. While we admit that poverty, in some cases, tends to make people slack, disorderly, and filthy, we deny that this is necessarily the case. The log cabin, with its rude, scanty furniture, may show marks of tidiness, as well as the mansion of the wealthy. And the scanty clothing may be clean. Though patch may be put upon patch, all may show the rough beauty and cleanliness of a hand and heart moved by the true spirit of reform.

But what can we say of the criminal carelessness of many professing Christians relative to their outhouses? We know of no language that will fully meet the case. We may write the words unhealthful, pestilential, terrible, horrible; but when compared with what the itinerant sometimes meets in August or September, such words really mean nothing. The sense of smell can sometimes recognize the existence of the poisonous, demoralizing abominations at a great distance.

By means of improper food, bad water, and impure air, diseases are received into the system. The food and water may be pure, but if the air is corrupt, the system will be poisoned, and, sooner or later, sickness must follow. In our frequent tours in New England, and throughout the Middle and North-western States, we have visited many sick persons. When searching for the cause of their ill health, if we failed to trace it to heredity, or to improper diet or impure water, we have usually found it in a bad condition of the outhouses. Whole families are often prostrated with fever, sometimes resulting in death to one or more of them, and yet the good people gravely and tearfully talk of the mysterious providence of God that has caused so much sickness, and removed kindred and neighbors, when the chief cause is in their own yard.

Often the barn and poultry yard are near the house, and the emanations from them, in connection with the vault usually found on the premises, are so foul that it is a wonder that any escape typhoid fever, which more frequently owes its origin to this cause than to all others. But what is worse, these abominations are sometimes so located that the drainage from them finds its way into the well. Among those so surrounded, health seems an impossibility. If a vault is used, it should be far from the well, and not too near the house ; and dry earth or wood ashes, used as a covering, will absorb the foul emanations. The directions given to the Hebrews concerning cleanliness, show how careful God was that the camp should not become contaminated, and should lead us to the utmost care as to the healthfulness of our surroundings.

We wish to arouse the people upon the subject of securing health, moral elevation, and happiness by providing themselves with the most healthful food, good water, and pure air. If they will do this, and be temperate in all their habits, they may give drugs to the dogs, save pain and money, and be able to say, "I am well."

Personal cleanliness by proper bathing is not only a healthful luxury, but a virtue. Again we quote Paul, where he connects physical and moral cleanliness : "Let us draw near with a true heart in full assurance of faith, having our hearts sprinkled from an evil conscience, and our bodies washed with pure water." *   The derivation of the word here rendered "washed," seems to have exclusive reference to washing from physical impurities. The effort of immersionists to press this text into the service of their mode of baptism, is an utter failure. Baptism by immersion does not *wash* the body.

Another apostle says of Christian baptism, It is "not the putting away of the filth of the flesh." †   The expression of Paul, then, "Having our hearts sprinkled from an evil conscience, and our bodies washed with pure water," refers to moral and physical cleanliness.

Between the altar of burnt-offering and the tabernacle of the congregation was the brazen laver, containing water in which the Jewish priests were to wash themselves before putting on the pure linen garments, preparatory to entering the sanctuary to minister before God, and it is distinctly stated that they must do this "that they die not." Here we are again impressed with the purity of God, and how particular he was to instruct the Hebrews that cleanliness was, to say the least, closely connected with acceptable worship.

Has the change of dispensations changed the character and mind of God in this respect? Has the death of his Son given license to Christians to pollute their bodies and souls with filthy indulgences, which in the former dispensation would have been prohibited on pain of death? — No! no!! God is the same in all dispensations. And those moral teachings found in the books of Moses, which contain rules to secure cleanliness, justice, holiness, and the favor of God, are as changeless as the eternal throne.

THE APPETITE IN HUMAN HISTORY.

THE history of the human appetite is indeed a sad one. The Creator designed that the appetite should be man's servant, not his master. It was to be subordinate to the moral and intellectual faculties. This truth is seen in God's first prohibitory declaration to man: "Of every tree of the garden thou mayest freely eat; but of the tree of the knowledge of good and evil, thou shalt not eat of it; for in the day that thou eatest thereof thou shalt surely die."*

God made man upright, and endowed him with powers of mind far above those of any other creature living upon the earth. He placed him upon probation, that he might form a character for the glory of the Creator, and for his own happiness. The first great moral lesson which the innocent pair of Eden were to learn, was self-control. God appeals to man's nobler powers. He graciously gives him all he needs for the delights of taste, and for the support of life. And it was for man's moral good, to say the least, that his eating from the tree of knowledge was prohibited. Of all the trees of the garden he might freely eat, *save one*. In this prohibition, the Creator places the appetite under the watchcare and guardianship of the moral and intellectual powers.

When man came from the hand of his Creator, he was declared to be "very good." He was put upon probation, that he might develop a perfect character. But he failed to do this. He basely yielded to the tempter, and lost his innocence; and the entire race, for six thousand years, have felt, in soul, body, and spirit, the taint of sin. The weight of accumulated guilt and ruin, resulting from continual transgression of moral and physical law, has rested upon it. Sickness, pain, sorrow, and death are the legitimate fruits of transgression.

* Gen. 2: 16, 17.

Man alone is responsible for the moral and physical wretchedness under which the race suffers. There was no necessity for Eve to yield to the tempter; and Adam is quite as inexcusable. The surroundings of our parents in Eden were delightful. The Infinite Hand had spread out before them a feast of pleasure in the stately trees, the climbing vines, and the beautiful shrubs and flowers. Eden also abounded with that which was "good for food." God had caused every good fruit-tree to grow, affording variety, and an inexhaustible supply. He welcomed man to eat freely of them all, excepting one only; but of the fruit of that *one* tree he warned him not to partake, on pain of death. Thus surrounded with beauty and plenty, and thus warned by the beneficent Author of his happy existence, man basely yielded, and plunged the race in consequent ruin.

Eve was flattered with the idea that eating the forbidden fruit would raise her to a higher and happier life. Appetite, curiosity, and ambition triumphed over reason. But Infinite Wisdom immediately devised the scheme of redemption, which placed man on a second probation, by giving him another trial, with the great Redeemer to help him in the work of forming a perfect character. And, to say the very least, it is reasonable to suppose that, in the second probation, men would be tested just where God tested our first parents in Eden, and that the indulgence of the appetites and passions would be the greatest moral evil in this world during the period of human probation.

We are not left to mere supposition in forming an opinion upon this subject. The sacred record shows, in the clearest manner possible, that God has tested his people since the fall just where he tested man before the fall, and that among the most flagrant sins of the fallen race, resulting in the greatest amount of human woe, has been the indulgence of appetite.

Gluttony and drunkenness were the prevailing sins of Sodom. It is said of the people of Lot's time, "They did

eat, they drank."* Appetite ruled them, or their eating
and drinking would not have been mentioned. For their
sins they were visited with destruction by fire and brimstone. It is also said of the people in the time of Noah,
"They did eat, they drank."* Gluttony and drunkenness
led to other crimes, and to wash the world from its moral
pollution, God poured upon it a flood of waters.

For the first twenty-five hundred years after the fall,
sacred history is exceedingly brief. For example, the life
and wonderful translation of holy Enoch are told in a few
lines. While, doubtless, the almost numberless good deeds
and careful acts of obedience in the long life of this wonderful man would furnish to some modern writers material
for volumes, the whole matter is summed up in these few
words: "All the days of Enoch were three hundred sixty
and five years: and Enoch walked with God; and he was
not; for God took him." †

We could not reasonably suppose that very much could
be said upon any one subject when the annals of twenty-
five hundred years, embracing many of the greatest events
in the world's history, are crowded into fifty short chapters of the Bible. But when God was about to establish
the tribes of Israel in the good land of promise, that they
should be to him "a peculiar treasure" above all people, "a
holy nation," the sacred historian speaks more fully, and
again the fact appears that God tests his people since the fall
just where he tested man before the transgression in Eden.

In the providence of God the sons of Jacob went
down into Egypt, where they sojourned in a strange land
for hundreds of years. There they were humbled by
slavery, but were delivered from it by the special hand
of Providence, and in the most triumphant manner. The
entire providential experience of the Israelites, both in
their servitude and in their miraculous deliverance, was designed to lead them to revere, and trustingly obey, the
God of their fathers.

The history of their departure from Egypt, the parting
of the Red Sea before them, and the destruction of their

* Luke 17: 28, 27.   † Gen. 5: 23, 24.

pursuers, is one of thrilling interest to all Bible Christians. These manifestations were designed to remove their infidelity, to draw them very near to God, and deeply to impress them with the fact that the Divine Hand was leading them.

God brought another test upon them in the gift of the manna. The Lord said to Moses, "Behold, I will rain bread from heaven for you ; and the people shall go out and gather a certain rate every day, that I may prove them, whether they will walk in my law, or no."* The habits of the Hebrews in Egypt had become such that a change to the simple manna was a very great one. But this change, God being judge of what was best for them, was necessary to their physical, mental, and moral well-being. God designed to bring a whole nation near to himself, and give opportunity for the development of perfect character. He tested the Hebrews on appetite, as he did man in Eden, and murmuring and rebellion resulted. Had they proved faithful to God, he would have taken them through the wilderness in the brief period of eleven days, and would have triumphantly planted in the land of promise the mighty host of Israel, whom he had borne "on eagles' wings" from Egypt. But they did not sustain the trial of their faith, and, in consequence of yielding to the clamors of appetite, they fell all along the way in the wilderness, so that only two of the adults who left Egypt were permitted to reach Canaan. I repeat it: the history of the human appetite is a sad one.

We here leave the Old Testament record upon this subject, after noting that in the Jewish age there were men of God who controlled appetite, as did the holy Daniel, who refused to defile himself with the king's meat and wine. Please read the first chapter of the history of this bold representative of pure hygiene.

The mission of John the Baptist was to prepare the way for the first advent of Christ. In the address of the angel to Zacharias relative to John, there is a brief chapter on hygiene: "Thou shalt have joy and gladness, and

* Ex. 16:4.

many shall rejoice at his birth. For he shall be great in the sight of the Lord, and shall drink neither wine nor strong drink."* It is said of this plain, temperate, yet mighty man of God : "The same John had his raiment of camel's hair, and a leathern girdle about his loins; and his meat was locusts and wild honey."† Some suppose that the prophet subsisted upon a sort of grasshopper diet, but this opinion may be seriously called in question. The following position seems to be sustained by good authority : —

"The locust was a fruit, a bean-like pod, with a seed in it similar to the *Carob*, or husk, on which the prodigal son fed." — *Butterworth.*

"Locust, *akris*, Gr., may either signify the *insect* called the *locust*, which still makes a part of the food in the land of Judea, or the *top of a plant*. Many eminent commentators are of the latter opinion."—*Clarke.*

At the very opening of the Christian age, the mission of Jesus is heralded by John, who sets an example of self-denial and temperance. The teachings of our Lord Jesus Christ and his holy apostles are in perfect accordance with the proposition that God, in all dispensations of probationary time, tests man just where he tested the innocent pair in Eden. "Take heed to yourselves," said the Son of God, "lest at any time your hearts be overcharged with surfeiting and drunkenness, and cares of this life, and so that day come upon you unawares."* And the words of Paul, addressed to the Christian church, make proper eating and drinking a matter of grave importance : "Whether, therefore, ye eat, or drink, or whatsoever ye do, do all to the glory of God."‡ The apostle argues in another place, that if there were no resurrection of the dead, there would be no future existence, and his laborious and abstemious life would bring him no future reward. He says, "What advantageth it me, if the dead rise not? let us eat and drink ; for to-morrow we die."‡ However much the apostle regarded it important to live temperately in order to a life of usefulness and happiness

* Luke 1 : 14, 15 ; 21 : 34.   † Matt. 3 : 4.   ‡ 1 Cor. 10 : 31 ; 15 : 32.

here, it is evident that he looked forward to the resurrection of the dead for the great reward of self-control. He says, in another place, "I keep under my body, and bring it into subjection; lest that by any means, when I have preached to others, I myself should be a castaway."*

But many of the professing Christian churches of this day treat this matter as though God had become discouraged in trying to lead men and women to a life of self-denial and self-control, and had changed his plan, no longer testing them upon the point of appetite, as formerly.

It is a humiliating fact that the moral powers of the majority of those who profess to be true followers of Christ, have become so far weakened by the indulgence of appetite and passion, that the most successful way to move them to acts of benevolence is through appeals to the appetite. Hence the almost universal custom of holding church festivals. These gluttonous feasts strengthen morbid appetite and inflame passion, and in the same degree weaken the moral powers, and benumb the finer sensibilities of the soul. The slave of appetite is moved less by such worthy and stirring considerations as the glories of the eternal world, the reward of philanthropic deeds in this life, and the final righteous retributions of a just God, than he is if treated with roast turkey, oysters, ice-cream, and the like. These charm his soul, and apparently open the closed avenues to his feelings of benevolence and to his purse, — a result which the worthy consideration of heaven, earth, and hell failed to produce.

If God is now testing professed Christians upon appetite, as he tested Adam and Eve and the Hebrews, then the case, with the exception of a decided minority, is a lost one. With the majority, the moral and intellectual powers are the servants, while the appetite is master. This was the condition of our first parents as they stood in Paradise lost, — the condition of the Hebrews who perished in the wilderness under the wrath of God. And in the light of the Scriptures these modern epicures are not

* 1 Cor. 4 : 27.

walking in the favor of God any more than were the per-
ishing Hebrews, or Adam and Eve when they coveted the
fruit which God had forbidden.

There are multitudes who are slaves to the expensive,
health-destroying, filthy habit of tobacco-using. Ninety-
nine out of one hundred of these will acknowledge the
evils of the practice. Then why not abandon the use of
tobacco?—Simply because the nobler powers are enslaved
by appetite. We have not a word of censure for men
who call in question the piety of those professed followers
of Christ who are controlled by appetite and passion.
Such do not truly represent the religion of the Bible.
The religion of our Lord Jesus Christ is entirely another
thing. The Redeemer of the world was tempted on all
points as we are, yet without sin. When tested in the
wilderness, he conquered, not on his own account, but for
us. And Christians are to overcome as he overcame.
That our adorable Redeemer might be able to succor his
tempted followers, and help them to overcome, he, in the
forty days' fast in the wilderness, endured the keenest
pangs of appetite. In him it is possible for the glutton,
the drunkard, and the poor inebriate of every stamp, to
overcome. With those who are ruled by appetite, and
who have not the help of Christ, the work of reform is
exceedingly doubtful. And we can hardly conceive of
anything more insulting to Heaven, than the profession of
the pure religion of the divine Son of God by men whose
reason and conscience are ruled by appetite and passion.

THE POWER OF APPETITE.

GOD designed that the appetite should be man's servant. When controlled by the moral and intellectual powers, it is one of God's blessed gifts; but when it becomes master, it is a debasing tyrant, crushing out of man that which is noble and God-like.

We go back in imagination over long ages, until we stand amid the glories of Eden before sin entered, and there we meet the painful fact that one of the weakest points in the character of Adam and Eve, while in all the perfection of manhood and womanhood, was the appetite. Their failure to exercise self-control upon this point — together with their curiosity and ambition — led to their fall. As the consequent moral darkness and downward tendency increased with each successive generation, the reign of appetite became more debasing and supreme. If appetite could move our first parents to an act of base disobedience, what must be its power over men and women of the nineteenth century, in whose physical, mental, and moral nature the taint of the fall still exists, with all the aggravations which have been acquired since Adam and Eve passed out of the gate of Paradise?

It is true that among the patriarchs and prophets were men who walked with God, and were the masters, not the slaves, of appetite, — like Daniel and his friends, who refused to defile themselves with the king's meat and wine. The apostles treat of Christian temperance in a most pointed manner. The apostle Paul says that "every man that striveth for the mastery is temperate in all things," and then adds, by way of application to the Christian life, "I keep under my body, and bring it into subjection, lest that by any means, when I have preached to others, I myself should be a castaway." *

We live in an age remarkable for Bibles, the Sacred Scriptures now being read in two hundred and fifty-two languages and dialects ; and yet there has probably never been a time when the people of Christian lands have been more completely under the rule of appetite. The gospel is preached everywhere. The present is said to be an age of wonderful light and gospel liberty ; but unfortunately, the gospel as too often preached in our time hardly touches the appetites and passions of men. And why should it, when so many of the teachers of religion do not feel called upon to renounce wine and tobacco or to restrain appetite ?

Many temperance men, with the waning cause of temperance as it relates to intoxicating drinks on their hands, are feeling that but little can be done in reforming drunkards, or in restraining young men from becoming such, while they indulge in the use of tobacco. The only way to cure men of the love of whisky is to restore the appetite to its natural state. And this can never be done while the common and free use of tobacco, tea, and coffee is continued. The only way to make real temperance men, is to teach the people to abandon all unnatural habits, and to use only those things which God designed for the use of man, and these in their natural state, as far as possible.

One has only to reflect a moment in order to be overwhelmed with astonishment at the unnatural, expensive, debasing habit of tobacco-using. We need not say that it is a filthy habit. If tobacco-chewers would only swallow that which is so sweet in their mouths, instead of spitting it out to the annoyance of cleaner people, their path would be less offensive ; but instead they eject on the street, in public places, and on the cars, that which is extremely odious to all who are not initiated in the disgusting habit.

* 1 Cor. 9 : 25, 27.

The habit is unnatural. Not one lad in a thousand liked tobacco when he first tasted it. And more than this, most boys suffer a terrible sickness, and pass a severe struggle, in taking their first lesson in tobacco-using. Then why do they form a habit so unnatural and disgusting? But one answer can be given: The habit is made respectable by judges, lawyers, ministers, doctors, and men of all ranks, and their influence is pressing our dear boys, with few exceptions, into this terrible vice. And these men, especially those who profess to be Christ's ambassadors, will have to answer for the result of their influence in the final settlement of the Judgment.

Nine hundred and ninety-nine of every one thousand tobacco inebriates would be glad to rid themselves of the habit; but they have become slaves to appetite, and have not the moral courage to persevere in that self-denial, and pass through that suffering, necessary to master the vice. We are not writing the condition of the few only. It is a painful fact that a majority of the men of our time have surrendered to the debasing rule of the appetite for tobacco.

"I know it is a filthy, expensive, and hurtful practice," said a minister, "and I would give three hundred dollars to be rid of tobacco; but the habit is formed, and I cannot overcome it." Officers were not wanting in our armies, during the late American war, who could lead their men into the hottest fight without the quiver of a muscle, and yet had not courage enough to break off the habit of tobacco-using. It is the mind that makes the man. Just in proportion as appetite and passion grow strong by excessive indulgence, the intellectual and moral powers are enfeebled. And in the same proportion as the moral and intellectual are strengthened by self-denial, healthy conditions are restored, morbid appetite is dethroned, and the chains fall off from the enslaved victim.

The restraints of the Sacred Scriptures, and the self-denial especially taught therein, are wanted to save men from the controlling power of appetite. The sentiments uttered by Christ and his apostles upon this subject are the purest of the pure : —

"If any man will come after me, let him deny himself." — *Jesus.*

"Let us cleanse ourselves from all filthiness of the flesh and spirit, perfecting holiness in the fear of God." — *Paul.*

"Abstain from fleshly lusts, which war against the soul." — *Peter.*

APPETITE CONTROLLABLE.

THE power of perverted appetite has been dwelt upon quite fully in the preceding chapter. Now it remains to be shown how the tyrant may be conquered. For it is possible for the appetite to be brought fully under the control of reason and conscience. The reclaimed drunkard, and those who have been emancipated from the slavery of tobacco, tea, and coffee, may shout greater victories than can the general who leads his troops through the most successful battles. An inspired proverb reads, "He that is slow to anger is better than the mighty; and he that ruleth his spirit, than he that taketh a city." * It may be said with equal truth and force, He that conquers perverted appetite is truly greater than he that conquers armies.

Difficult as the task may be, a morbid appetite can be restored to a normal condition. As it is by indulgence that appetite gains the mastery, so it is only by rigid abstinence that it can be conquered and made man's servant. As in the one case indulgence is the cause, and the debasing rule of appetite the result; so in the other case abstinence is the redeeming cause, and natural appetite (controlled by reason and conscience), health, and happiness are the glorious result. But the man of strong habits, who undertakes to grapple with and conquer his appetite for fashionable indulgence, may as well understand at the very start that he has a hard battle to fight; and he should count the cost, lay well his plans, and nerve himself for the contest.

And there is a very important fact which we wish here to state for the encouragement of those who feel the need of reforming in habits of life, and who at the same time dread the difficulties in the way, and the suffering they may have to endure. It it this: Proper abstinence will soon give them complete victory; and when this is gained, when simple and natural habits have been established, the delights of taste and the pleasures of existence will far exceed the so-called enjoyments found in a gross and unnatural life of hurtful indulgence.

When the drunkard leaves his cup, he suffers inexpressible physical and mental agony until by continued abstinence and proper habits the fire dies out of his blood and brain, and nature restores order. This accomplished, the reformed inebriate has lost his love for liquor, and feels that he is a man again. It is not to be questioned that the man who satisfies his depraved cravings for whisky, feels a momentary pleasure in indulgence; but the enjoyments of existence, with him whose habits are natural and healthful, are almost infinitely greater than with him who is ruled by morbid appetite, and who surrenders to the momentary pleasure found in its gratification.

Here are facts of the greatest importance; and they are not only in harmony with natural law, but are sustained by the happy experience of many a reclaimed drunkard. It is difficult to make the drunkard, even in his soberest hours, see and feel the force of these facts. His friends may wish to help him; but he alone must fight the battle with appetite, or he can never enjoy the victory. The higher powers of his mind are benumbed and enfeebled, having been surrendered to the rule of appetite. He, however, decides to make the effort to reform, and abstains from liquor for a few days. He is in agony; and feeling no assurance that, if he perseveres, the period of his suffering will be brief, he is in danger of yielding to the erroneous idea that abstinence dooms him to a life-long period of mental and physical agony. Oh to get across this, to him, impassable gulf! The fields of delight which lie beyond, he cannot now see; but when fairly across, he may shout victory in the midst of the natural and healthful pleasures of an almost new existence. This is one of the greatest triumphs that mortal man can achieve, and one long step toward heaven. Yet such a victory can be won.

What has been said in the case of drunkenness is equally true of tobacco inebriety. The appetite for tobacco will continue so long as the tobacco poison remains in the system. When the system has been freed from tobacco by abstinence and hygienic treatment, the appetite will cease. Boys have a natural dislike for tobacco, but this they overcome by its use. When their blood becomes thoroughly poisoned, the collision between nature and tobacco ceases. Completely eradicate tobacco from the human system, restore the taste to a natural and healthful condition, and tobacco will be as offensive to its emancipated slave as to the youth before he took the poison into his blood.

Let no one try to overcome the appetite for tobacco by the long, tedious, murderous process of "leaving off by degrees." Victory is seldom, if ever, gained in this way. Total abstinence is the only sure course. Hygienic treatment is of great benefit to those who find this a difficult task. In order to obtain a speedy and certain victory, the poison should be taken from the blood as soon as possible. Water treatment will do this at a rapid rate. We have left tobacco invalids packed in the wet sheet forty minutes, and when they were taken out the scent of tobacco so pervaded the room as to be sensible to the taste, and the sheet itself was discolored.

What has been said about the liquor and the tobacco habit is true, in the main, in the case of those addicted to the use of tea and coffee. Total abstinence is the only remedy. When these habits are overcome, and restoration, so far as possible, to natural conditions takes place, whisky, tobacco, and tea and coffee sicknesses, in their many forms, will cease. For example, there are thousands of women in our country who once drank strong tea to cure the headache, and it did give them temporary relief; but at the same time it laid the foundation for more severe headache. Now they use neither tea nor coffee, and can

bear the joyful testimony that when they had by abstinence overcome their desire for tea, their headache also
disappeared.

Those on our side of the question, who have passed
through the struggle against the clamors of morbid appetite, and have gained the victory, can appreciate this
view of the subject. Those on the other side must pass
over to us, and work out their own experience before
they can fully understand the matter.

And right here is where the subject of hygienic reform
meets one of its greatest obstacles. It is difficult for those
under the control of appetite to see anything in the
reform but privation and starvation. They sit down to a
hygienic dinner, — without flesh-meats and highly seasoned
gravies, — where all the food is, so far as possible, in its
natural state, and are disgusted with its tastelessness.
They pity us who live upon this diet, and, judging by
their own condition of taste, are grieved that we are
starving ourselves. But the very dinner they despise, we
enjoy with the keenest relish, and do it liberal justice.

To us who have become accustomed to a simple, unstimulating diet, it would be painful to sit down to a
fashionable dinner and partake of highly seasoned flesh-
meats. The very spices, salt, vinegar, pepper, mustard,
and pickles that would delight a fashionable taste, would
be very unwelcome to ours. The great difficulty in this
subject is, that those who differ with us cannot understand
the matter fully until they have, through their own experience, come all the way over to our side of the
question.

To all hygienic reformers I would say, Live up strictly
to the convictions of your own enlightened mind. Be not
led into indulgence by the entreaties of friends. Live
the reform at home ; and when you go abroad, carry it
with you. Live it, and at proper times, in proper places,
and in a proper manner, talk its principles. Never let
the opposition or the kind entreaties of friends, gain
ground on you. Ever hold on your way, and by all

proper means labor to impress those around you with the importance of the subject.

A few words to those who are making changes: If you make them all at once, be sure to make a corresponding change in your mental or physical labor. If your circumstances are such that you cannot greatly lessen your labor for a while, or spend a few months at a sanitarium, you should, in matters of diet, make the changes gradually. But do not forget to change. As you prize health and the favor of God here, and a happy existence in his presence in the next world, turn from the violation of natural law. Let it be your study and constant effort to bring your habits of life more and still more into harmony with the laws instituted by the beneficent Author of your being.

THE GOSPEL OF HEALTH.

"To him that overcometh will I grant to sit with me in my throne, even as I also overcame, and am set down with my Father in his throne." * This text presents two grand themes, — overcoming, and the victor's reward. The magnitude and importance of the work of overcoming are measured by the value of the reward presented. The human mind cannot conceive a reward of greater value than that here offered. It is to be exalted to the throne of the Son of God, when he shall reign King of kings and Lord of lords. Christ will then wear his kingly crown, and the overcomer will also wear a crown. Christ will reign, and the overcomer will reign with him. This reign of peace, of exaltation, of glory, in which the overcomer is to participate, will continue throughout the ceaseless rounds of eternal ages. And all this glory is presented to us as an inducement to engage earnestly in the great work of overcoming.

Christians generally have a very indefinite idea of what it is to overcome, in the sense of the text. With few exceptions, they seem never to think that it has reference to self-control, and especially to the complete control of appetite. Hence, professing Christians eat fashionable viands, smoke, chew, and snuff tobacco, drink tea and coffee, become gluttons and drunkards, and thus defile the temple of God, † simply to gratify depraved appetite. And many of these Christians, doubtless, regard the work of overcoming as very nearly summed up in mastering their embarrassment in speaking and praying in public, and saying grace over their fashionable tables. God pity them!

The text, however, gives a definite idea, in plainest terms, of what it is to overcome, — "even as I also overcame." Men and women are to overcome as Christ

* Rev. 3 : 21.   † 1 Cor. 3 : 17.

overcame. When we are able to comprehend the temptations and victories of the Son of God, we shall have a definite idea of what it is to overcome. The subject of Christ's overcoming may be discussed under three propositions : —

1. The Son of God did not overcome on his own account. He was not a sinner. He "was in all points tempted like as we are, yet without sin." The divine Son of God was so far a partaker of our nature as to feel our woes and suffer for our sins, yet in him was no sin, and his overcoming was not for himself.

2. The work of overcoming on the part of the Son of God was on account of our sins. The temptations he suffered and the victories he gained, were to enable him to succor mortal men and women suffering under the weakness of the flesh, and beset with strong temptations. The apostle speaks definitely on this point : "For it became Him, for whom are all things, and by whom are all things, in bringing many sons unto glory, to make the Captain of their salvation perfect through sufferings." "Wherefore in all things it behooved him to be made like unto his brethren, that he might be a merciful and faithful high priest in things pertaining to God, to make reconciliation for the sins of the people. For in that he himself hath suffered, being tempted, he is able to succor them that are tempted." "For we have not a High Priest which cannot be touched with the feeling of our infirmities ; but was in all points tempted like as we are, yet without sin."* The divine Redeemer was subjected to the fiercest temptations, passed through the most fearful struggles, and gained victories the most glorious, that he might redeem man from the ruin of the fall, the weaknesses of the flesh, and the temptations of the devil.

3. As the Captain of our salvation, Christ has led the way in the work of overcoming. And in order that he might succor the tempted, he has been tempted in all points as we are. This was not for his own benefit, but for our good. Therefore our temptations are, in kind,

* Heb. 2 : 10, 17, 18 ; 4 : 15.

just what the Son of God endured; and the victories
which we must gain in overcoming, are, in kind, just what
the Son of God experienced when he overcame. This
proposition is most fully sustained by the clause, "as I
also overcame," found in our text.   Having clearly before
the mind the idea that the divine Redeemer, as the Captain of our salvation, has led the way, subjecting himself
to the very temptations and self-denial which his followers
must experience in order to be redeemed by his blood,
let us consider the temptations of the Son of God, and
the circumstances under which he overcame.

Immediately after his baptism in Jordan, "Jesus was
led up of the Spirit into the wilderness, to be tempted of the
devil." *   The record of another evangelist reads, "Immediately the Spirit driveth him into the wilderness.   And
he was there in the wilderness forty days, tempted of
Satan, and was with the wild beasts." †   Another evangelist gives the facts of the temptations of Christ in still
another form, "Jesus, being full of the Holy Ghost, returned
from Jordan, and was led by the Spirit into the wilderness,
being forty days tempted of the devil.   And in those
days he did eat nothing." ‡

The Holy Spirit led the Son of God into the wilderness, to be tempted of the devil.   This was a part
of the great plan necessary to the salvation of sinners.
The temptation must occur as truly as the crucifixion,
the resurrection, the ascension, or the second advent.
The crucifixion of Christ and his intercession for sinners
are subjects of very common and popular discussion in the
pulpit and by the religious press; but the temptation of
Christ in the wilderness, though holding an important
place in the great plan, is passed over as having little
more significance than if it were an accidental occurrence,
—as if Christ chanced to be in the wilderness just then,
and Satan seized upon the opportunity to annoy him.
But mark well the strong expression of Luke: "Jesus being
full of the Holy Ghost returned from Jordan, and was led
by the Spirit into the wilderness."

There in the wilderness, wild, barren, and dreary, the Son of God endured the first of the three great temptations that represent the leading temptations to which the fallen race is exposed. For want of space, I can here dwell only on this first temptation, which relates to appetite. Satan urged Christ to work a miracle by changing stone to bread to satisfy the pangs of hunger after the fast of forty days. Christ resisted the temptation. The Saviour's long fast, the temptations under the peculiar circumstances, and the victory gained, were not only a part of the great plan by which Christ became the Redeemer of the lost race, but they were designed to present an example full of encouragement to those who have still to struggle against the power of appetite.

The grandest thought in all the range of revealed theology is, that Christ in his life on earth was tempted on all points as mortal men are, in order that he might be "able to succor them that are tempted." In that long fast in the wilderness, our Saviour endured the keenest pangs of hunger, in order to save sinners lost by indulgence of appetite, — that his arm might reach to the depths of wretchedness and weakness, even of the poor glutton and the miserable drunkard.

The Redeemer, both divine and human, as an over-comer in our behalf, stood in the very position where Adam's failure plunged the race into ruin. Christ endured the very test under which Adam failed. He took hold of redemption just where the ruin began, and succeeded in carrying out the plan.

The subject is truly grand. At thought of these things, there kindles in the soul the most ardent love, and the deepest reverence for our all-conquering King. He over-came on our account. He leads the way in suffering, mental agony, victory, and triumph, and bids us follow in self-denial and everlasting glory. We hear from him by way of Patmos, saying, "To him that overcometh will I grant to sit with me in my throne, even as I also overcame, and am set down with my Father in his throne."

Mark well these vital points on this subject : —

1. Christ did not overcome on his own account, but for us.

2. His temptations and victories were to enable him to succor his tempted people.   Therefore, —

3. His temptations were in kind just what his people must meet and overcome.

The victory of our triumphant Head over the most subtle temptations during his forty days' fast, and the glorious promise of reigning with him in his throne, on condition that we overcome *as* he overcame, establish the fact that one of the highest attainments in the Christian life is to control appetite, and that, without this victory, all hope of heaven is vain.

Is there suffering and self-denial in the work of over-coming ?   The Christian will joyfully welcome these, in view of heirship to the eternal throne and the crown of glory.   "If we suffer, we shall also reign with him."   "But rejoice, inasmuch as ye are partakers of Christ's sufferings; that, when his glory shall be revealed, ye may be glad also with exceeding joy." *

* 2 Tim. 2 : 12; 2 Peter 4 : 13.

REDEMPTION.

To redeem is to purchase back from sale or from slavery; to deliver from the bondage of sin or its penalties. God proposed to redeem the fallen race through the sacrifice of his Son. This great redemption is threefold: First, from the condemnation and practice of sin; secondly, from the grave; and thirdly, from the disgrace of the fall.

1. Redemption from the condemnation and practice of sin. "Sin is the transgression of the law." * The apostle doubtless refers particularly to the moral code; yet the transgression of any law established by our beneficent Creator to govern our actions, is sin. Said the angel, referring to the Redeemer, "Thou shalt call his name Jesus; for he shall save his people from their sins." † The mission of the Son of God was to save man *from*, not *in*, the transgression of law.

Man fell under the power of appetite. The Redeemer set his people an example of self-denial, and he says to them, "Whosoever will come after me, let him deny himself, and take up his cross, and follow me." ‡ But what of those who profess to be followers of Jesus, but are really drunkards and gluttons? How does the Master esteem those who gratify appetite without regard either to expense or to the physical and moral influence of such a course upon themselves and their children? Ministers and people, clergy and laity, chew, smoke, and snuff the "filthy weed," simply because it produces, for the time being, a pleasant sensation. They pollute their breath, their blood, their clothes, their dwellings, and the atmosphere of even their places of worship, to gratify morbid taste. Slaves to tobacco! The moral and intellectual in servitude to the animal! The Protestant, church-going people of America pay out more money annually for

---

* 1 John 3:4.   † Matt. 1:21.   ‡ Mark 8:34.   (207)

tobacco, tea, and coffee, to poison their blood, than for the gospel of Jesus Christ, to purify their lives. Professed Christians will yield to the clamors of appetite for luxuries and indulgences which stupefy their higher powers and strengthen the baser passions, and at the same time they will talk piously of the self-denial and cross of the Christian life! This certainly falls but little short of a burlesque upon the Christian religion. In the words of Charles Beecher, "O unhappy church of Christ! fast rushing round and round the fatal circle of absorbing ruin! Thou sayest, 'I am rich, and increased in goods, and have need of nothing; and *knowest not* that thou art poor, and miserable, and blind, and naked'!"

"Know ye not," says Paul, "that ye are the temple of God, and that the Spirit of God dwelleth in you? If any man defile the temple of God, him shall God destroy; for the temple of God is holy, which temple ye are."* Again the apostle appeals to the church at Corinth in these words: "Beloved, let us cleanse ourselves from all filthiness of the flesh and spirit, perfecting holiness in the fear of God."†

To those, and to those only, who by self-control turn from a life of excess, and choose a life of self-denial and purity, will the atoning blood of Christ be applied. It is said of the numberless hosts of the saved, that they "washed their robes, and made them white in the blood of the Lamb."‡ The robes of character were not given to them for the occasion, to hide their sins. No; *they washed their* robes.

Some of the rich blessings which it is the privilege of Christians to enjoy in this life are mentioned in these stirring, triumphant words of Paul: "That ye might be filled with the knowledge of his will in all wisdom and spiritual understanding; that ye might walk worthy of the Lord unto all pleasing, being fruitful in every good work, and increasing in the knowledge of God; strengthened with all might, according to his glorious power, unto all patience and long-suffering with joyfulness; giving thanks

---

*1 Cor. 3 : 16, 17.   † 2 Cor. 7 : 1.   ‡ Rev. 7 : 14.

unto the Father, which hath made us meet to be partakers of the inheritance of the saints in light : who
hath delivered us from the power of darkness, and hath
translated us into the kingdom of his dear Son ; in whom
we have redemption through his blood, even the forgive-
ness of sins." *

And the beloved John declares the message that " God
is light, and in him is no darkness at all." " If we walk
in the light, as he is in the light, we have fellowship one
with another, and the blood of Jesus Christ his Son
cleanseth us from all sin." † The Redeemer, in overcoming, set an example of self-control to his followers,
and then closed his life of disinterested benevolence by
death on the cross. Here is seen his matchless love for
sinners. Those who deny themselves, who overcome as
he overcame, and by faith wash their robes of character
and make them white in his blood, may sing of redeeming
power and love here, and they will find eternal ages none
too long to swell the happy strain, " Worthy, worthy is
the Lamb ! "

2. The redemption from the grave, by the resurrection
to immortal life, of all who are in this life redeemed from
the condemnation and practice of transgression, is the
second stage in redemption. It is in this life that we
obtain a moral fitness for the next. The change to
immortality is not a moral change ; it is simply an exchange of the corruptible body for one that is incorruptible. This second stage in the Redeemer's stupendous
achievement of man's redemption, is expressed by the
apostle thus : " Who shall change our vile body, that it
may be fashioned like unto his glorious body." ‡

3. The redemption of the righteous from the disgrace
of transgression completes the work of the Redeemer.
The redeemed are then on higher and safer ground than
that on which Adam stood before his fall. In the estima-
tion of God, of Jesus, angels, and all created intelligences
in the universe, they stand the same as if our first
parents had not disgraced themselves and their children

* Col. 1 : 9-14.　　† 1 John 1 : 5, 7.　　‡ Phil. 3 : 21.

by yielding to the power of appetite. The Redeemer has borne their sin and shame, and has accepted, in his own sinless person, the punishment due them. Man's failure to form a righteous character was complete. Jesus took man's place, and endured the test; his success in working out a righteous character in man's behalf, is as complete as was Adam's failure. To those who, in a life of self-denial and self-control, have by faith followed their triumphant Head, the righteousness of Christ is imputed. In their Saviour the redeemed lose all their shame and disgrace. Not only will they then stand complete in the purity of their own robes of character, which they have washed and made white in the blood of the Lamb, but they will shine with the brighter luster of the divine righteousness and eternal glory imputed to them from their adorable Redeemer.

HYGIENIC REFORM:

ITS RISE AND PROGRESS AMONG SEVENTH-DAY ADVENTISTS.

[WHILE the reformatory principles held by Seventh-day Adventists are in no way peculiar to them, it is probable that this people present a unique example of the adoption, by a religious denomination, of a body of health principles requiring a radical change of habits, and affecting the lives of individual members in all their physical relations. The careful reader of the preceding pages of this volume will hardly need to be informed of the sources from which the health principles of the denomination have been drawn; but it will nevertheless be profitable to consider more at length the development of this remarkable movement among this people.

Fortunately, the task of tracing the history of this reform was undertaken, years ago, by one eminently qualified for its execution; and we cannot serve our readers better than by presenting the substantial part of what was then written by Elder James White in a series of articles which appeared in the pages of the *Health Reformer* during the years 1870 and 1871. To these articles will be appended a brief sketch of the growth of the movement since that time, and the development of the various new and important phases which have naturally grown up from the foundation laid by the pioneers of this great reformatory enterprise.]

Every real reform — every movement that tends to improve man's present condition or to affect his future happiness — is under the direct providence of God. This is true of the great cause of hygienic reform. Though Jews, Turks, skeptics, Christians, or modern Judases, who would sell their Lord for money, may act a part in it, the reform, nevertheless, is of God.

It is with great pleasure that we consider this matter from a Bible point of view. The Bible is to us the voice of Infinite Wisdom, the highest and safest authority ; and it contains a vast amount of testimony touching the subject of health. Christian temperance is taught on almost every page of the New Testament. We thank God for science ; and we also thank him that, on the subject of hygiene, science and the word of God are in harmony.

Seventh-day Adventists have not felt that it was safe to base their hope of salvation upon mere theories of the future life, or upon a belief in the arguments which prove that that immortal state is near. They have felt the necessity of a preparation for the great realities of the future, and have made this a matter of practical consideration. Now is the time to obtain that moral fitness which is necessary for the change of " our vile bodies " at the coming of our Lord. The moral change must take place now, in order to the change to immortality then.

Admitting that we are living in that brief period divinely allotted to the work of preparing for the second advent of the Son of God, and the change to immortality, how timely is the introduction of the subject of hygienic reform among us, — a reform which changes false habits for those of Christian temperance, and purity of soul, body, and spirit !.

Look at the picture of Noah's time and ours, presented in Matt. 24 : 37-39 : "As the days of Noah were, so shall also the coming of the Son of man be. For as in the days that were before the flood, they were eating and drinking, marrying and giving in marriage, until the day that Noah entered into the ark, and knew not until the flood came, and took them all away ; so shall also the coming of the Son of man be." The great sins of the men and women of the Noatic world, when God poured upon it a flood of waters and washed it from its moral pollution, were drunkenness, gluttony, and the indulgence of sensuous passions. The intellectual, the moral, the God-like, in man were brought down to serve the animal appetites and passions. The sins for which the antediluvians were condemned, are the leading sins of our own time. This is emphatically an age of drunkenness, gluttony, vice, and crime. Yet, thank God, in the midst of the moral filth and wretchedness, there are those who feel the force of the divine warning, — "Take heed to yourselves, lest at any time your hearts be overcharged with surfeiting [gluttony], and drunkenness, and cares of this life, and so that day come upon you unawares." *

The glories of the future life are promised us on condition that we turn away from popular pollutions. "Wherefore, come out from among them, and be ye separate, saith the Lord, and touch not the unclean ; and I will receive you, and will be a Father unto you, and ye shall be my sons and daughters, saith the Lord Almighty. Having therefore these promises, dearly beloved, let us cleanse ourselves from all filthiness of the flesh and spirit, perfecting holiness in the fear of God." †

Would we be the adopted sons and daughters of the Almighty? Then we must shun the excesses of this degenerate age, and perfect that holiness which consists in physical as well as moral cleanliness. Our God is the embodiment of purity. Into heaven "there shall in no wise enter . . . anything that defileth." ‡ The throne of God, the tree of life, and the river of life, clear as crystal, will be charming in their purity. We believe it to be but a little while to the ushering in of the day of immortal blessedness ; and should we not feel unutterable longings for that purity of flesh and spirit which is necessary in order to be meet for the inheritance of the saints in light? With this in view, no one should marvel that Seventh-day Adventists are a denomination of hygienic reformers.

* Luke 21 : 34.   † 2 Cor. 6 : 17, 18 ; 7 : 1.   ‡ Rev. 21 : 27.

The denomination known as Seventh-day Adventists has existed about twenty-two years; as an organized body, only ten years. Rising from a very small beginning, its members in the United States now [1870] number about fifteen thousand. From the first, some of the principles of hygienic reform have been cherished,˙ but it is only about five years since the general change in diet and the reform in dress.

Seventh-day Adventists took up the subject of hygiene from religious principle, and they adhere to it in the love and fear of the God of the Bible. They have a living, growing interest in the reform as taught among them, because of its harmony with science, with their own invaluable experience, and with the word of God. Their ministers teach it to the people publicly and at the fireside, and they practice it, so far as possible, wherever duty calls them. This people also carry out the reform in their social relations with kindred and friends, at home and abroad. This straightforward course makes them practical as well as theoretical teachers of hygienic reform. And this is no more than might be expected. A people who have moral courage to leave the deep rut of human custom, and observe the seventh day of the week as the Sabbath of the Lord, purely from principle, should be found firm and true in all reforms. To be out of joint with the rest of the world for two days in each week, is neither convenient nor profitable. The observance of the Bible Sabbath is frequently attended with pecuniary loss. It is also decidedly unpopular; and nature shrinks from taking a step that carries one so far from the world. And the high sense of truth and duty that leads this people to a conscientious observance of the Sabbath of the Bible, also leads them to adopt and carry out the principles of hygienic reform.

Seventh-day Adventists have taken their position upon unpopular points of theology from hearing sermons and reading works which appeal to their moral and intellectual faculties. The grand themes upon which they dwell with delight and profit are the comparison of prophecy with history ; the origin, nature, and perpetuity of the divine law ; and that purity of flesh and spirit which is requisite to heirship to the future inheritance.

While thousands are induced to take a position in matters of religion simply because their feelings are wrought upon, and while tens of thousands adopt a religion simply because it is popular, Seventh-day Adventists are moved by appeals to the noblest powers of the human mind. Such a people should be ready to follow truth wherever it may lead them, and properly to estimate reforms wherever they may exist. And having, from reason and conscience, taken their position on the subject of hygienic reform, they are prepared to defend it, and to reap the benefits of it.

As a people, we have discarded the use of tobacco in all its forms. Thank God for so glorious a victory over perverted appetite ! In the annual assemblies of the leading men of our denomination, not the least taint of the filthy weed can be discovered by sight or smell. Our people have also discontinued the use of tea and coffee, as unnecessary, expensive, and injurious to health. Here another victory has been gained.

This work of reform has entered at least four thousand families among us, and saves an expense of not less than twenty-five dollars annually to each family, making the entire sum saved in one year about one hundred thousand dollars. This is indeed a handsome sum to give for the cause of humanity and religion. When the benefits of emancipation from the slavery of morbid appetite are taken into the account, we, as a people, can afford to double the sum, and give two hundred thousand dollars as a tribute to the blessings of hygienic reform.

But the reform among us does not stop here. Our people have put away the use of swine's flesh, and, to a great extent, of flesh-meats generally. This they have done from a conviction that flesh is not the most nutritious or the most healthful food for man. While flesh-meats stimulate, they do not build up the system, as other foods do. This was once an experiment with our people ; now it is demonstrated.

Seventh-day Adventists have adopted two meals a day, instead of three. But this is not a denominational law with them, as their church organization and discipline have nothing to do with regulating such matters. Yet in most cases they discard flesh-meats, and partake of food but twice each day. These facts we have learned from personal observation in holding camp-meetings with them from Maine to Kansas, during the past summer. Our ministers preach hygienic reform, and live it wherever they go. And our many publications carry it to the doors of all our people. Thousands have testified to the benefits of the changes they have made. They report better health, and an increase of physical strength. Ask them if they can perform as much labor without meat and without the third meal as they could before they made these changes, and they will tell you that since their present habits have become fully established, they can endure more labor, and that they enjoy life much better. This is the experience of all, whether professional or laboring men.

God designed our sleeping hours to be a period of complete rest to the entire being, stomach and all. But let one eat the third meal, and then go to bed ; do the digestive organs rest ?—No. Other parts of the system rest ; but that mill of a stomach must grind the grist on hand, or still greater evils will result. So it grinds, while its owner imperfectly sleeps. He turns restlessly from side to side. The brain sympathizes with the overworked stomach. Bad dreams follow, perhaps nightmare ; and in the morning the supper-eater wakes with bad feelings in the stomach, faintness, foul breath, depression of spirits, and perhaps sick-headache. He feels condemned for something, he knows not what. In fact, if domestic matters do not move off smoothly, he is decidedly cross. The birds sing, but he does not hear them. The glorious sun comes up, but what of that ? This is no more than it has done every morning for six thousand years. With a heavy heart and a sad countenance he takes up the duties of the day.

There is no good excuse for habitual morning head-ache. When you sleep, let the stomach rest, as well as all other parts of the system. Take two full, healthful meals each day, and let all your other habits be temperate and correct, and we shall hear as little of headache as of handache or footache. Labor, physical or mental, may throw the blood to the brain, and the weary man may go to rest with aching head. But if his stomach be not loaded with the third meal, and if the entire man be per-mitted to enjoy rest while he sleeps, the blood will retire from the head, and he will awake in the morning free from pain, rested and refreshed with sleep, from the crown of his head to the sole of his foot. He feels not only the restoring influence of sweet sleep in his entire being, but he is in possession of a moral benefit which is beyond price. He wakes with a clean stomach, a clear head, a free heart, a clear conscience (if he deals justly, loves mercy, and walks humbly with God), and a buoyant spirit. The language of his soul is, "Let everything that hath breath praise the Lord."* How delightful to such a man is the dawn of a summer morning! He wakes to join the happy songsters as they warble forth their morn-ing praise to nature's God. He meets the rising sun again with gladness, and greets the members of his household with feelings of tenderness and love. And thus he goes forth to the duties of the day, enjoying health of body and mind, feeling that he is a man, and competent for the tasks of life.

It is true that the miseries of this life are made up of the natural results of many sins; but we solemnly believe that prominent among these is the sin of gluttony, especially in the form of the third meal. In a moral point of view, this sin is a terrible one. It debases the man, and makes him earthly, sensual, devilish. To eat and drink fashionably, — that is, of that which was not

* Ps. 150:6.

designed as food for man, — and too often, is an outrage upon the stomach. It deranges the digestive machinery, benumbs and beclouds the moral and intellectual powers, strengthens and inflames the passions. That which is God-like in man is brought down to serve the lower instincts.

Many persons of strong constitution who are engaged in active, out-door labor, do not appear to be much affected by wrong habits of eating and drinking. Some of them may live to old age ; but in many cases, these wrong habits result in nervous dyspepsia, followed by physical and moral evils which seriously affect the Christian life. The dyspeptic suffers depression of spirits, and often falls into a desponding mood, which sometimes ripens into despair. Such persons cast a shadow, instead of giving light to the world. They are, in fact, a burden to themselves and to all around them. The influence of these gloomy, desponding, dyspeptic Christians goes far to impress the minds of the youth with the idea that religion is calculated to deprive them of real happiness, and that it is totally unsuited to their years.

I solemnly believe that ninety per cent of the existing despondency, despair, and what is called religious insanity, is caused by the abuse of the stomach. He who looks through smoked glass sees nothing bright and pleasant. The beauties of nature and of art all look stained and gloomy. So the dyspeptic Christian views God, Christ, angels, and heaven through a brain beclouded by continued abuse of the stomach.

But the man who is ignorant of the facts in the case cries out that those who have undertaken a reform in diet, are starving themselves to death ! Let us see. My own table is furnished fourteen times each week from the following varieties, prepared by an intelligent cook, in every inviting form : —

Vegetables. — Potatoes, turnips, parsnips, onions, cabbages, squashes, peas, beans, etc.

Grains. — Wheat, corn, rye, barley, oatmeal, rice, farina, cornstarch, and the like.

Fruits.—Apples, pears, peaches, strawberries, raspberries, blackberries, huckleberries, grapes, cranberries, raisins, and tomatoes.

Besides these, we keep one of the finest young cows in Michigan, which is fed and treated in a manner to secure to our family of twelve, about ten quarts per day of the best milk. We starve to death?—Not we. "But can you afford these extras?"—Indeed we can. They do not cost, the year round, as much as the old diet of flesh-meats, spices, etc. But this is not our reason for the change. The object of hygienic reform is not to save money, but to secure health, manhood, purity, and heaven.

When the subject of healthful diet and two meals a day was first introduced among Seventh-day Adventists, it was favorably received by the majority. This was owing, in a great measure, to the manner in which it was presented. Mrs. White was the first to speak upon the subject among our people. She went from State to State, speaking once or twice at each of our large gatherings. She appealed to the people upon the subject of Bible temperance, dwelling upon the great benefits and blessings to be derived from correcting bad habits of life. The subject was a fruitful one, and was presented in a happy, earnest style. She spoke to men and women who held the Bible as the highest and safest authority, and there were few who objected to her teachings. Many immediately left the use of flesh-meats, and adopted the two-meal system. Several of our ministers, who had been afflicted with disease, soon reported a better state of health as the result of changing their habits of life. The interest was very general, and seemed to be steadily increasing.

In the year 1865, Mrs. White prepared a work of four hundred pages, entitled, "How to Live." It was first issued in six pamphlets, to subscribers, by the Seventh-day Adventist Publishing Association, Battle Creek, Mich. These pamphlets were devoted, one each, to the questions of food, bathing, drugs, air, clothing, and exercise. A large edition was printed, and a portion of it was bound in a neat volume, which had a large sale. It was readable, and well adapted to meet the wants of the people. It had a wide circulation outside of Seventh-day Adventists, and its influence for good, in calling attention to the subject of hygienic reform, can hardly be estimated.

Another book published about this time was a little work of sixty-four pages, entitled, "An Appeal to Mothers. The Great Cause of the Physical and Moral Ruin of Many of the Children of our Time." This also was prepared by Mrs. White, and a large edition was issued by the same publishers. Many personal friends scattered the work very widely, because of the confidence they had that the author was especially taught of the Lord. Others assisted in its circulation, because of the truth which it earnestly set forth. Thousands of youth have read this pamphlet, and many have been reformed by it. Thousands of mothers have had their attention called to the importance of taking every precaution to save their young children from falling into evil habits and polluting vices. The warning has been faithfully given, and its good results are already evident.

In the early part of 1865 I became fully satisfied that I had received great benefit from adopting the principles of hygienic reform, so far as we understood them. I had been afflicted with rheumatism, and with difficulties of the stomach and head. These were disappearing, and I enjoyed clearness of thought, freedom of spirit, and physical strength and activity. This great improvement in health led me to intemperance in labor. To my former arduous duties was added an active effort to teach the people the principles of hygienic reform. This was put forth in the form of lectures upon the subject in the morning and between religious services at our State Conferences.

At this time, while I was making important changes, my labors should have been decreased, instead of being increased. I was exploring a new field, ignorant of the

dangers to which I was exposed. But with ardent zeal
I labored on. One morning, after a constant strain on
my mental and physical powers, as Mrs. White and myself were enjoying our usual walk, I suffered a stroke of
paralysis. My right arm was rendered useless for a short
time, and the brain and the power of speech were so far
affected that I could utter but one word to the faithful
friends who gathered around, and that was, Pray. After
a short season of prayer, relief came, so that I could raise
the paralyzed arm, and could imperfectly converse. But
dyspepsia in its worst form followed, and in three months
I was reduced over fifty pounds in weight. In this condition I continued for about one year. But by the blessing of God, and careful attention to the laws of health, I
was finally enabled to rally. During the past three years
I have dispensed with flesh-meats, and have taken but
two meals a day. I have worked hard and incessantly, as
few men do, and have come up from one hundred and
thirty-four pounds to one hundred and eighty.

During the fifteen months of my severe sickness, Mrs.
White was by my side ; and of course she was necessarily
silent, so far as public labors were concerned. Hence the
work of pushing forward hygienic reform among Seventh-
day Adventists devolved upon others. And some of those
who undertook to guide the movement were so unfortunate
as to adopt extreme positions, and, in some localities,
brought reproach upon the cause.

These extremes operated against the reform in two
ways : First, they caused a great amount of prejudice ;
and, secondly, in the minds of many who were but partially converted to the reform, they furnished an excuse
for drawing back to former habits of life. It is a great
misfortune for those who labor to move minds in any
good cause, to run to extremes. Our work is to move
the people ; and the more people we can reach, the more
good is accomplished. If reformers must err at all, it is
safest for their own influence, and much better for those
they would help, to err on the side nearest the people. If

they err on the other side, they at once place themselves where they cannot reach the people at all. Some may be satisfied to take extreme positions, and stand in their defense, with the few who adhere to the same, leaving all the rest of the world uninstructed upon the broad principles of reform; but such a course does not commend itself to my mind.

One thing is certain, instructors should practice their own teachings before urging them upon others. And then, when they become fully established, and live out strictly their own sentiments, when they have learned to value them highly, and feel the importance of teaching them to others, they should labor judiciously to lift the people up to them. Have they reached a firm footing above their friends, and do they rejoice in a higher position than they occupied but yesterday? then they should remember the "hole of the pit" from which they have just been taken. We were all beginners once. The cause is a progressive one. As we advance, let us take as many of the people with us as possible.

In every society or association of men there are always novices ready to seize upon the most extreme thoughts and suggestions; and with a spirit more keen than tolerant, they will urge their views at any time, anywhere and everywhere. These persons appear never to think of the words of the Divine Teacher, "I have yet many things to say unto you, but ye cannot bear them now."* They do not learn the truth contained in them, — that the human mind is not always ready to receive even important truths. Christ labored to lead his disciples forward step by step, as they could understand the new truths he was ever opening before them. He understood the philosophy of the mind, and he knew how to deal with it.

Not all are prepared to teach. There are a hundred who should take the learner's seat, where there is one adapted to the teacher's stand. Many who talk loud and long of reform would be better qualified for the work

* John 16:12.

after learning something to say that would shed clear light upon the subject; while others fail entirely in their efforts to teach the people, from a want of mental discipline, and of experience in dealing tenderly with other minds. "He that winneth souls is wise." *

All questions upon which people are sensitive should be treated with candor and great care, even by those who are well-informed, and competent to teach, lest the minds of those they would instruct should be closed by prejudice. But on the subject of hygiene, which restricts the appetites and passions of men, double care should be taken by those qualified for the work, to "speak the truth in love."

In the early days of the reform, there were errors and extremes in practice as well as in theory. We might refer to the cold-water men of from twenty to thirty years ago. Better-informed hydropathists now talk of less "heroic" treatment, — tepid water, and more pleasant baths. When water-treatment was first introduced, novices were, in some instances, guilty of remaining all night in a cold, wet-sheet pack, and that, too, by the consent of their friends. They would come out in the morning trembling with cold. It is a wonder they did not die outright. Cold water, applied in a proper manner, during a proper period of time, is indispensable in some diseases, and for some persons. But cold water improperly applied has death in it.

What is true of extremes in the use of water, is also true in a degree of extremes in diet. And it is a matter of the deepest regret that the public mind has been soured by the advantages that have been taken of existing extremes, and that good men and women have become prejudiced against the true philosophy of life and health.

The cause of hygienic reform, however, is onward, and all enlightened and sincere reformers will follow on in the path of light and right. The changes from injurious habits of life to those conducive to health, are great, and should be made with care, especially if the same habits

* Prov. 11 : 30.

of labor are continued. It is always best to labor much less at the time of changing to a vegetarian diet, and adopting two meals a day. Is a man a tobacco user, a tea-and-coffee drinker, a meat eater, taking his three meals? Let him begin with tobacco, and put that away. Then let him leave off the use of tea and coffee, eat less meat, and make his third meal very light. He will find this a heavy tax upon his system. He may all the time *feel* worse; but what of that? There is a glorious victory ahead. Soon he can dispense with flesh-meats altogether. His appetite will become natural, and he can take simple, healthful food with a keen relish. Next, he leaves off the third meal. As he sleeps, his stomach rests; and in the morning he does not suffer from faintness, as when his stomach was taxed with the third meal. When right habits of diet are established, and the victory over morbid appetite is gained, the morning hours, especially in summer, are the happiest and best.

Shall we stop here? Having gained victories, and now enjoying many of the blessings resulting from a change from wrong habits of life, how natural and consistent that we should still look forward to higher and yet holier attainments in life and happiness!

The attention of our people was first called to the harmful effects of tea, coffee, and tobacco about twenty years ago. For thirteen years the voice of truth, pleading in the name of Christian temperance, was heard among us, warning us against these slow poisons, before our attention was called to any further advance in habits of life. This was all that could be borne till victory should turn in favor of purity and health, and against these popular evils. The good work went steadily on, until our tables were cleared of tea and coffee, and our homes and persons were free from the stench of tobacco.

Our dwellings and our places of worship are no longer defiled with the filthy narcotic. Here we will join the song of jubilee with our mothers, daughters, and sisters, that our homes are redeemed from this defilement, and that fathers, sons, and brothers are free from the scent of the baneful weed, and, in this respect at least, are pure and manly.

We forbear to enter into all the details of domestic wretchedness occasioned by the slow, but sure, process of enfeeblement, disease, nervousness, and fretfulness occasioned by the use of tea and coffee. Thank God that our sisters have found a happy release from these subtle enemies of health and happiness! With improved health, free from the tea headache, in the enjoyment of firmer nerves and a calm spirit, they will now allow husbands, sons, and brothers, in their turn, to rejoice.

If personal cleanliness only were involved in this matter, both men and women might well thank God for victories gained. But here are principles to be maintained that reach beyond the exterior, — principles that affect our well-being not only in this life but in the life to come.

When we say that those who have found freedom from the tyranny of tea, coffee, and tobacco, enjoy improved health, clearer brains, and more even and buoyant spirits, we state a fact to which thousands among us can bear testimony. But the good work of reform did not end here. About seven years ago, the attention of our people was especially turned to the importance of thorough ventilation, and to the relation of proper food and clothing to health. The question of flesh-eating came up, and was fully and candidly discussed. It was decided that flesh was less nutritious than bread, — an opinion sustained not only by the best medical authorities in our country and Europe, but by the experience of thousands who have tested the matter for themselves. While we admit that flesh is a food, we deny that it is the best food for man. It stimulates the system, but does not nourish and build it up, as do grains, fruits, and vegetables. Besides this, animals are liable to be more or less diseased; and by partaking of their flesh, man receives their diseases into his own system.

It is stated upon good authority that while wheat, corn, barley, rye, and oats contain seventy-five parts nutrition and twenty-five parts waste, pork, beef, and mutton contain only twenty-five parts nutrition and seventy-five parts waste. On this hypothesis, one pound of meal contains as much nutriment as three pounds of meat. The poor man may figure thus: The rich pay fifty cents for three pounds of meat, which contain no more value in nutrition than one pound of good, unbolted wheat-meal, costing only four cents. Again, the poor man may reason from established facts It takes five pounds of corn fed to swine to make one pound of pork. Three pounds of the pork contain no more nourishment than one pound of cornmeal; therefore it is a hard trade to throw away fourteen-fifteenths of the golden blessing of a liberal Providence, and save only one-fifteenth for hungry children, and that, too, in the form of scrofulous swine's flesh.

Bu it may be argued that one feels stronger immediately after eating liberally of flesh. This is admitted. The same is true of tea and whisky. It is also true that the languor which follows the stimulating influence of tea and whisky is felt in a degree by those who subsist largely upon flesh-meats. On this point also the writer can speak from experience. After breakfasting largely upon beefsteak, feelings of faintness used to call for a lunch by eleven o'clock. Now, after a breakfast at 6:30 A. M., of vegetables, fruits, and bread, nothing more is needed till 12:30. And it is the testimony of hundreds whose digestion is feeble that the faintness they felt when eating flesh three times a day, has subsided since abstaining from meat entirely, and taking only two meals a day of grains, fruits, and vegetables.

Let no one imagine, however, that all the benefits of hygienic reform are to be realized in a day, in a week, or even in a year. It may take five or ten years for those who suffer from wrong habits of living to prove the good results of conforming to nature's laws. Once these changes were an experiment with our people, but the experience of years has demonstrated their importance. The longer the blessing that results from these changes is enjoyed, the more clearly it is seen, and the higher is our estimate of its value.

HEALTH INSTITUTIONS.

In the summer of 1866, through the influence of Mrs. White, the foundations were laid for the first health institution among Seventh-day Adventists. Indeed, the institution founded at that time was one of the first of the sort in the western part of the United States. Perhaps it may be said that it was the first of the kind in the United States, or in the world, as it possessed many unique features, and was not conducted as a money-making scheme. Between thirty and forty thousand dollars was raised for the enterprise by the friends of health and temperance reform. A proper site was selected, and the Health Institute opened in August, 1866.

During the first years of the institution, water was almost the sole remedial agent employed, and a large number of persons were restored to health by a careful use of baths, and the healthful regulation of diet, rest, exercise, and general habits of life. After ten years of very successful work as a water-cure, the institution was reorganized under a new management and with a broader scope. The name was changed from "Health Institute" to "Medical and Surgical Sanitarium." Since that time the managers have undertaken to supply to their patients all known rational remedies for disease. The facilities for treatment have been constantly enlarging, but at no time have they been more than sufficient to meet the rapidly growing patronage of the establishment. The four original wooden buildings have given place to two fine brick structures, capable of accommodating several hundred sick people.

At the time of this writing, the family of the institution, comprising patients, nurses, and attendants, numbers more than six hundred persons. Nearly four hundred thousand dollars is invested in buildings and medical appliances, and competent persons, who visit this institution after having visited the principal medical establishments of the world, declare unhesitatingly that there is no establishment in the civilized world which equals this in the extent and completeness of its facilities for the care of the sick.

Several years ago the managers, finding themselves unable to accommodate the increasing demand for skilled nurses and attendants, established a Training School for Nurses, which has grown to be the largest school of its kind in the United States. At present, nearly one hundred nurses are employed in the Sanitarium. The Training School numbers more than eighty pupils. The course of training in this school is so thorough that its graduates are in constant demand. Almost daily the managers receive calls for nurses from various parts of the United States, which they are unable to supply. Scores of young men and women have already received training for most useful and lucrative positions, and the reputation of the school is such that the managers are able to receive only a small proportion of those who apply.

A Training School in Domestic Economy is also conducted in connection with the institution, in which young men and women are trained in the art and science of economic housekeeping. This department comprises one of the most excellent cooking schools in the United States, and is in session the year round. Scores of young men and women from various European countries, as well as from different parts of the United States, are in constant attendance at these schools.

Still another line of educational work is the Sanitarium Kindergarten, in which children are taught and trained after·the most healthful methods for developing both the mind and the body. The managers of this department have recently organized a course of instruction for young women who wish to devote themselves to this branch of educational work.

A course of instruction is also carried on for the purpose of fitting persons to engage in health and temperance missionary work. This course comprises not only instruction in the principles of hygiene and temperance, but gives a training in the best methods of imparting instruction to others by means of talks, conversations, readings, and the distribution of health literature.

The generosity of 'the stockholders in relinquishing their dividends to be used for charitable purposes, has enabled the managers to extend the advantages of the institution to hundreds of worthy persons who are poor. The work in this department, since the organization of the institution, amounts to more than one hundred thousand dollars, or nearly three times the whole original capital stock as a self-supporting work. The success of this enterprise is unrivaled, and its charities are constantly extending into new lines, as fast as the funds of. the institution will allow.

In the year 1877 a health institution, based upon essentially the same principles as the Sanitarium at Battle Creek, was established at St. Helena, Cal. This institution, known as the Rural Health Retreat, has developed into a large and flourishing establishment, capable of caring for one hundred invalids, and hundreds of sick people have been restored to health through its agency. Another institution has been recently opened at Mt. Vernon, Ohio; and several small establishments, mostly of a private character, have sprung up in various parts of the United States, being carried on by those who have been connected, more or less, with the original health institution at Battle Creek. Plans are now in operation for the establishment of a branch institution in some part of Colorado.

HEALTH JOURNALS.

About the time of the establishment of the first health institution, the publication of a journal, known as the *Health Reformer*, was begun, with the object of promulgating the principles of health and temperance reform which were advocated and practiced at the Health Institute. The journal soon acquired a large subscription list, and became one of the most widely circulated health publications in the United States. About the time of the reorganization of the Health Institute, the name of the journal was changed to *Good Health*, under which title it is now published. Probably no other journal of the kind wields so wide an influence in the interests of health and temperance and social purity reform, as this.

Eight or nine years ago a health journal in the Danish language was started in Christiana, Norway. This soon became so popular that it was necessary to publish an edition also in the Swedish language. More recently, two journals in the Scandinavian languages have been started in this country, so that now there are four health journals in those languages, and each has a wide circulation.

Several years ago the managers of the Rural Health Retreat established a journal known as the *Pacific Health Journal*, which has reached a liberal circulation, and has accomplished much in the dissemination of the principles of health and temperance reform.

In addition to the various journals mentioned, books, tracts, and pamphlets have been issued by the hundred thousand.

Before leaving this subject, it will be proper to call attention to a prediction made by Mrs. White more than twenty years ago, regarding the health institution at Battle Creek: "With all the efforts in every department, put forth in a correct and judicious manner, and with the blessing of God, the institution will prove a glorious success." Another statement, made before the institution had reached half its present dimensions and facilities, is as follows: "If it [the Sanitarium] is conducted in a manner that God can bless, it will be highly successful, and will stand in advance of every other institution of the kind in the world."

The following article from Mrs. White clearly sets forth the principles upon which the Sanitarium should be conducted : —

A HEALTH INSTITUTION.

In a vision given me Dec. 25, 1865, I saw that Seventh-day Adventists should have a home for the sick, where they could receive medical care, and also learn how to live so as to prevent disease ; that it should be an institution whose influence would be closely connected with the work of fitting mortals for immortality ; and that it should not be established for the object of gain, but to aid in bringing God's people into such a condition of physical and mental health as will enable them rightly to appreciate eternal things, and correctly to value the redemption so dearly purchased by the sufferings and death of our Saviour. Unless this object should be continually set before the people, and efforts made to this end, the institution would prove a curse instead of a blessing.

Health reform is a part of the great benevolent, sacrificing work of God ; and this institution, incorporated for the special purpose of diffusing light upon this question, should prove itself a factor in this charitable work. Donations given to it should be considered a sacrifice to God, the donors looking for their dividends in his kingdom. The institution itself should be charitable, doing all it can for the relief of the worthy poor. Physicians, managers, and helpers should all work on the same liberal, sacrificing plan, not merely for money, but for the glory of God and the relief of their suffering fellow-men.

Why should the Christian physician, who is waiting and longing for the coming and kingdom of Christ, when death will no longer have power over the saints, expect more remuneration for his services than the Christian minister or editor ? He may say that his work is more wearing ; but God does not require any man to work beyond his strength, in any employment. He should work as he can endure, and not violate the laws of life which he teaches to his patients. There is no good reason why he should overwork and receive high wages for it, more than the minister or the editor.

No one who labors simply for money should be suffered to remain at the Sanitarium as a helper. There are those of ability, who, for the love of Christ, might fill positions of trust faithfully and cheerfully, and with a spirit of sacrifice. Those who have not this spirit should withdraw, and give place to those who have it.

It is God's design that the Sanitarium which he has established shall stand forth as a beacon of light and warning and reproof. He would prove to the world that an institution conducted on religious principles as an asylum for the sick, can be sustained without sacrificing its peculiar, religious character; that it can be kept free from the objectionable features that are found in other institutions of the kind. It is to be an instrumentality in his hand to bring about great reforms.

The Lord has shown me that in an institution established among us, the greatest danger would be that its managers would depart from the spirit of the present truth, from that simplicity which should ever characterize the disciples of Christ. The prosperity of the Sanitarium is not dependent alone upon the intelligence and knowledge of its physicians, but upon the favor of God. If it is conducted in a manner that God can bless, it will be highly successful, and will stand in advance of every other institution of the kind in the world. Great light, great knowledge, and superior privileges have been given; and in accordance with the light received will be the accountability.

The instruction given me concerning it, contained a special warning against lowering the standard of truth in any way in order to meet the ideas of those not of our faith, and thus secure their patronage. But if they choose to come where religion is exalted, and where the managers carry out Bible principles in all departments of the work, they place themselves directly under the influence of the truth; and many, besides obtaining relief from bodily infirmities, will also find a balm for their sin-sick souls. One precious soul saved will be worth more than all the means contributed toward the establishment of such an institution. The Sanitarium, if rightly conducted, may be the means of bringing important truths before many whom it would be impossible to reach by ordinary methods. While our faith should not be urged upon the patients, nor any religious controversy forced upon them, our papers and publications, carefully selected, should be in sight almost everywhere. The religious element must predominate.

I have seen that physicians and helpers should be of the highest order,— those who have an experimental knowledge of the truth, who will command respect, and whose word can be relied on. They should be free from jealousy and evil-surmising, — persons who have a power of will that does not yield to slight indispositions, who are unprejudiced, who think and move calmly and considerately, having the glory of God and the good of others ever before them. Those only should be chosen to responsible positions who are qualified to fill them ; and they should first be proved, to see if they are free from jealousy and favoritism.

Those who treat the sick should constantly seek the blessing of God upon their work, expecting him to aid them in the use of the means he has so graciously provided, and to which he has specially called our attention as a people, — pure air, cleanliness, healthful diet, adequate rest, and the use of water. They should allow no selfish interest to divert their attention from this important and solemn work. To care properly for the physical and spiritual interests of the afflicted who place themselves under their care, will require their undivided attention. No one has so great a mind, or is so skillful, that the work will not be imperfect, even after he has done his best.

Let those to whom are committed the physical, and also to a great extent the spiritual, interests of the afflicted people of God, beware how they, through worldly policy or personal interest, or a desire to be engaged in a popular work, call down upon themselves the frown of God. They should not depend upon their skill alone. If the blessing of God is upon the institution, holy angels will attend patients, helpers, and physicians, to assist in the work of restoration, so that in the end the glory will be given to God, and not to feeble, short-sighted man.

Wrong habits of life are to be corrected, the morals elevated, the tastes changed, the dress modified. A great amount of disease is brought into the world through the prevailing style of dress; and the fact should be made prominent that a reform must take place before treatment can effect a cure. The crippled, diseased organs of the body, and the dwarfed faculties of the mind, cannot be strengthened and invigorated without decided reforms. Those who are connected with the Sanitarium should be in every respect correct representatives of the principles advocated there.

I saw the beneficial influence of out-door labor upon those of feeble vitality and poor circulation, especially upon women who have induced these conditions by too much confinement in-doors. Their blood has become impure for want of fresh air and exercise. Instead of inventing amusements to occupy the patients in-doors, employment should be afforded them in cultivating the ample grounds around the Sanitarium; and this labor should be made a part of their prescription. Flowers, fruit, and vegetables might be raised, under the direction of an experienced gardener, and thus afford employment appropriate to the sex and condition of every one.

While the Sanitarium may have patronage from people of wealth, there are many among us who are not able to pay the expenses of a journey thither, and a lengthened stay. Shall poverty keep these friends of our Lord away from the blessings which he has so bountifully provided? Shall they be left to struggle on with the double burden of sickness and poverty? Those who are wealthy, and have all the conveniences and comforts of life, may, by taking home treatment, often enjoy a very fair state of health. But it is our poor brethren, who have hardly the necessaries of life, that need our help. They may have faults, and yet may be living up to duty better than some who have means ; and many of them are humble Christians.

The expenses of some of these should be defrayed by the churches to which they belong. Some, again, have rich relatives to whom they can look for assistance. But there are many others who have no such resource ; and for these a fund should be provided by those to whom God has intrusted means.

The stay of such at the Sanitarium must necessarily be short. By means of the lectures they hear, and by securing good books, they can learn how to live at home ; and on their return they can carry out the principles they have learned there. They must not rely on the physician to cure them in a few weeks, but must learn to live so as to give nature a chance to work the cure. It may require years to complete the healing process begun at the Sanitarium.

But those who receive the benefits of this liberality, must be willing to be taught. They should cherish a spirit of gratitude to God and to their brethren for the help they receive. They should understand that their sickness and poverty are misfortunes, often caused by their own sins and their ignorance of the laws of health; and if the Lord puts it into the hearts of his people to help them, it should inspire in them a spirit of gratitude.

Let no one entertain the idea that the Sanitarium is the place to be raised up by the prayer of faith. It is rather the place to find relief from disease by treatment and right habits of living, and to learn how to avoid sickness. But if there is one place under heaven more than another where sympathizing prayer should be offered by men and women of devotion and faith, it is at such an institution. I have seen that the reason why God did not more frequently answer the prayers of his servants for the sick among us, was that he could not be glorified in so doing while they were violating the laws of health. He designed health reform and the Sanitarium to prepare the way for the prayer of faith to be answered. Faith and good works should thus go hand in hand in relieving the afflicted among us, and in fitting them to glorify God here, and to be saved at the coming of Christ. God forbid that these afflicted ones should ever be disappointed and grieved in finding the managers working only from a worldly standpoint, instead of adding to the hygienic practice the blessings and virtues of nursing fathers and mothers in Israel.

PERSONAL EXPERIENCE.

The following sketches of the lives of Elder Bates and Elder Andrews were written by Elder James White in 1877, and appeared in the pages of *Good Health* of that year : —

ELDER JOSEPH BATES.

SKETCHES of the lives of great and good men are given to the world for the benefit of the generations that follow them. Human life is more or less an experiment to all who enter upon it. Hence the frequent remark that we need to live one life in order to learn how to live. This maxim, in all its unqualified strength of expression, may be a correct statement of the case of the self-confident and incautious ; but it need not be wholly true of those who have had good and wise parents, and who have proper respect for the prudent and good people who have made life a success. To those who profit by the experiences of those who have fought the good fight, and have finished their course with joy, life is not altogether an experiment. Its general outlines, to say the least, may be patterned after those who have, by the grace of God, become good and noble and truly great, in choosing and defending the right.

Reflecting young men and women may acquire, even before they leave parental care, a practical education which will be invaluable to them in future life. This may be done to a considerable extent by careful observation ; but in reading the lives of worthy people they may learn lessons by which they will be fortified against the evil, and be enabled to choose the good, that lies all along the path of human life.

Second to our Lord Jesus Christ, Noah, Job, and Daniel are held up before us by the sacred writers as patterns worthy of imitation. The brief sketches of the faith, patience, firmness, and moral excellence of these and other holy men, as found in the pages of sacred history, have been proved to be of inestimable value to all who would walk worthy of the Christian name. They were men subject to like passions as we are. Were some of them, at times, overcome of evil? erring men of our time may bless that record also; for it states how these ancient worthies overcame evil, and fully redeemed their errors, so that, becoming doubly victorious, they shine brightest on the sacred page.

In his epistle to the Hebrews, Paul gives a list of heroes of faith. In chapter eleven he mentions Abel, Enoch, Noah, Abraham, Isaac, Jacob, Joseph, Moses, and the prophets, who through faith subdued kingdoms, wrought righteousness, obtained promises, and stopped the mouths of lions. The apostle presents these witnesses as patterns for the Christian church, as may be seen by the use he makes of them in the first verse of the chapter which follows: "Wherefore, seeing we also are compassed about by so great a cloud of witnesses, let us lay aside every weight and the sin which doth so easily beset us, and let us run with patience the race that is set before us."

Since the apostle's time, there have been many who exemplified in their life the same firm principles for which the ancient worthies were commended. Elder Joseph Bates was such a man. His life was crowded with unselfish motives and noble actions. That which makes his early history intensely interesting to his personal friends, is the fact that he became a devoted follower of Christ, a thorough reformer, a Christian gentleman, and ripened into a noble manhood, and all this while exposed to the evils of sea-faring life, — from the cabin-boy of 1807 to the wealthy retiring master of 1828, a period of twenty-one years.

Beauty and fragrance are expected of the rose, planted in suitable, well-cultivated soil, and tenderly reared under the watchful eye of the lover of the beautiful; but it is with wonder that we admire the living green, the pure white, and the delicate tints of the water-lily, whose roots reach far down into the cold mire at the bottom of the darksome lake. And we revere the Power that causes this pearl of flowers, uncultivated and obscure, to appropriate to itself all valuable qualities, and to reject the evil.

So, to apply the figure, we reasonably expect excellence of character in those who are guarded against corrupting influences, and whose surroundings are the most favorable to mental and moral development. In our hearts, pressing up to our lips, are blessings for all such. But he who, in the perpetual presence of the uncultivated and vile, and with no visible hand to guard and guide, becomes pure and wise, and devotes his life to the service of God and the good of humanity,— a Christian philanthropist,—such a one is indeed a miracle of God's love and power.

Joseph Bates was born July 8, 1892. The following brief account of his parentage and boyhood is taken from his "Autobiography," published in 1868 :—

"My honored father and his forefathers were for many years residents in the town of Wareham, Plymouth County, Massachusetts. My mother was the daughter of Mr. Barnabas Nye, of the town of Sandwich, Barnstable County, both towns but a few hours' ride from the noted landing-place of the Pilgrim Fathers.

"My father was a volunteer in the Revolutionary War, and continued in the service of his country during its seven years struggle. When Gen. Lafayette revisited the United States, in 1825, among the many who were pressing to shake hands with him at his reception rooms in the city of Boston was my father. As he approached, the General recognized him, and grasped his hand, saying, 'How do you do, my old friend, Captain Bates?' 'Do you remember him?' was asked. His answer was something like the following: 'Certainly; he was under my immediate command in the American army.'

"After the war, my father married and settled in Rochester, an adjoining town in Plymouth County, where I was born. In the early part of 1793 we moved to New Bedford, some seven miles distant, where my father entered into commercial business.

"During the war with England, in 1812, the town of New Bedford was divided, and the eastern part was called Fairhaven. This was ever afterward my place of residence until I moved with my family to Michigan, in May, 1858.

"In my school-boy days my most ardent desire was to become a sailor. I used to think how gratified I should be if I could only get on board a ship that was going on a voyage of discovery round the world. I wanted to see how it looked on the opposite side. Whenever I thought of asking my father to let me go to sea, my courage failed, for fear he would say, No. When I tried to unburden my mind to my mother, she endeavored to dissuade me, and proposed some other occupation. At last they permitted me to accompany my uncle on a short trip to Boston, hoping this would cure me ; but it had the opposite effect. My parents then complied with my wishes.

"A new ship, called the Fanny, of New Bedford, was about to sail for Europe ; the commander, Elias Terry, agreed with my father to take me on the voyage as cabin-boy. In June, 1807, we sailed from New Bedford to take our cargo on board at New York City, for London, England."

With increasing interest we follow young Bates in his perilous experience upon the seas, and recognize in him a spirit firm and undaunted, ready to live up to his convictions of right, and we also see the hand of Providence in wonderful deliverances from danger and death. At one time he had the courage, under trying circumstances, to reject a bribe offered to induce him to take a false oath ; and by testifying to the truth he saved the fore-fingers and thumb of his right hand, with which he wrote during his long life in advocating and defending the noblest reforms of the age. He says : —

"While we were congratulating ourselves respecting our narrow escape from shipwreck, two suspicious looking vessels were endeavoring to cut us off from the shore. Their cannon balls soon began to fall around us, and it became advisable for us to round to and let them come aboard. They proved to be two Danish privateers, who captured us and took us to Copenhagen, where ship and cargo were finally condemned in accordance with Bonaparte's decrees, because of our intercourse with the English.

"In the course of a few weeks we were all called to the court-house to give testimony respecting our voyage. Previously to this, our supercargo, who was also part owner, had promised us a handsome reward if we would testify that our voyage was direct from New York to Copenhagen, and that we had had no intercourse with the English. To this proposition we were not all agreed. We were finally examined separately, my turn coming first. I suppose they first called me into court because I was the only youth among the sailors. One of the three judges asked me in English if I understood the nature of an oath. After I had answered in the affirmative, he bade me look at a box near by, about fifteen inches long and eight high, and said, 'That box contains a machine to cut off the two forefingers and thumb of every one who swears falsely here. Now,' said he, 'hold up your two forefingers and thumb on your right hand.' In this manner I was sworn to tell the truth, and regardless of any consideration, I testified to the facts concerning our voyage. Afterward, when we were permitted to go aboard, it was clear enough that the 'little box' had brought out the truthful testimony from all; viz., that we had been wrecked by running against an island of ice fourteen days from New York; refitted in Ireland, after which we joined the British convoy, and were captured by the privateers. After this, some of our crew, as they were returning from a walk where they had been viewing the prison, said that some of the prisoners thrust their hands through the grating, to show them that they had lost the two forefingers and thumb of their right hand. They were a crew of Dutchmen, who were likewise taken, and had sworn falsely."

As the primary object of this sketch is to present Elder Bates to the reader as a true reformer, we pass over the perils and shipwrecks, the captures and imprisonments by sea and on land, the scenes of great suffering and providential escape, during the first eight years of his sailor life, up to the time he rejoined the home circle in June, 1815. Speaking of this time he says : —

"My father had been told by those who thought they knew, that if I ever did return home I would be like other drunken man-o'-war sailors. Our meeting quite overcame him. At length he recovered, and asked me if I had injured my constitution. 'No, father,' I replied, 'I became disgusted with the intemperate habits of the people I was associated with. I have no particular desire for strong drink.' This much relieved his mind."

In 1821 Joseph Bates became master of a vessel, and sailed on a voyage to South America. Not only did he have charge of the ship, but the cargo also was confided to him for sales and returns. Of his convictions on the subject of total abstinence from ardent spirits, he says : —

"While on our passage home, I was convicted of a serious error, in that I had for more than a year allowed myself to drink ardent spirits, although I had before practiced entire abstinence, having become disgusted with the debasing and demoralizing effects of strong drink, and being well satisfied that drinking men were daily ruining themselves, and moving with rapid strides to the drunkard's grave. Although I had taken measures to secure myself from the drunkard's path by not allowing myself in any case whatever to drink more than one glass of ardent spirits per day, which I most strictly adhered to ; yet the strong desire for that one glass, when coming to the dinner hour, the usual time for it, was stronger than my appetite for food, and I became alarmed. While reflecting about this matter, I solemnly resolved that I would never drink another glass of ardent spirits while I lived. It is now about forty-six years since that important era in the history of my life, and I have no knowledge of ever violating that vow, having never since used spirits, except for medicinal purposes. This circumstance gave a new spring to my whole being, and made me feel like a free man. Still it was considered genteel to drink wine in company."

The mind of the youthful master was evidently guarded from corrupting influences, and deeply impressed by a high and holy power. The associations in which his position placed him were such as to make it almost impossible for him to keep his solemn pledge, yet he did not waver. The true spirit of reform had taken hold of him, and he moved out still further. On the passage from Buenos Ayres to Lima, Peru, in 1822, he gained another victory, of which he speaks as follows : —

"As I had resolved on my previous voyage never more to use ardent spirits except for medicinal purposes, so now I also resolved that I would never drink another glass of wine. In this work of reform I found myself entirely alone, and exposed to the jeering remarks of those with whom I afterward became associated, especially when I declined drinking with them. Yet after all their comments, that it was not improper or dangerous to drink moderately, etc., they were constrained to admit that my course was perfectly safe."

While in Peru, several months after he had resolved to leave off wine also, our hero was severely tested. His statement, which follows, shows that instead of wavering and yielding to the pressure of associates, he took another firm step in reform : —

"Mr. Swinegar, our Peruvian merchant, gave a large dinner party to the captains and supercargoes of the American vessels, and to a number of the officers of the American squadron, Feb. 22, in honor of General Washington's birthday. As I was the only person at the table who had decided not to drink wine or strong drink because of its intoxicating qualities, Mr. S. stated to some of his friends that he would influence me to drink wine with him. He filled his glass, and challenged me to drink. I responded by filling my glass with water. He refused to drink unless I took the wine. I said, 'Mr. Swinegar, I cannot do so; for I have fully decided never to drink wine.' By this time the company were all looking at us. Mr. S. still waited for me to fill my glass with wine. Several urged me to comply with his request. One of the lieutenants of the squadron, some distance down the table, said, 'Bates, surely you will not object to taking a glass of wine with Mr. Swinegar.' I replied that I could not do it. I felt embarrassed and sorry that a cheerful company should be so intent on my drinking a glass of wine as almost to forget the good dinner that was before them. Mr. S., seeing that I would not be prevailed on to drink wine, pressed me no further.

"At that time my deep convictions with respect to smoking cigars enabled me to decide also that from that evening I would never smoke another cigar, nor smoke tobacco in any way. This victory raised my feelings and elevated my mind above the fog of tobacco-smoke which had to a considerable extent beclouded my mind, and thus I was freed from an idol which I had learned to worship among sailors.

"I had now been in the Pacific Ocean about fourteen months, and was closing my business and preparing to return to the United States. The ship Candace, Capt. F. Burtody, was about to sail for Boston, Mass., in which ship I engaged my passage. Capt. B. and myself mutually agreed, when the Candace weighed anchor, that we would from that hour cease chewing tobacco. About the last week of November, 1823, all hands were called to weigh anchor. None but those who experience these feelings can tell the thrill that fills every soul, from the captain to the cabin-boy, when the order is given to 'weigh anchor for home.' No matter how many seas there are to pass, or how many storms to meet, or how far from home, the joyous feeling still vibrates in every heart, 'Home, home, sweet home! Our anchor's weighed for home!'

"Our good ship now lay by with her main topsail to the mast, until the boat came alongside from the commodore with our specie and silver, which Capt. B. and myself had gained by trading. When this was safe on board, all sail was made on the ship. It was now night, and we were passing our last landmark (St. Lorenzo), and putting out for a long voyage of eight thousand five hundred miles. The steward reported supper ready. 'Here goes my tobacco, Bates,' said Capt. B., taking it from his mouth and casting it overboard. 'And here goes mine, too,' said I, and that was the last that ever polluted my lips. But Capt. B. failed to overcome, and labored hard to induce me to keep him company. I was now free from all distilled spirits, wine, and tobacco. Step by step I had gained this victory. Nature never required either, and I never used the articles, except to keep company with my associates. How many millions have been ruined by such debasing and pernicious habits! How much more like a human being I felt when I had gained the mastery in these things, and overcome them all!

"I was also making great efforts to conquer another sin, which I had learned of wicked sailors. That was the habit of using profane language. My father had been a praying man from the time I had any knowledge of him. My mother embraced religion when I was about twelve years old. I never dared, even after my marriage, to speak irreverently of God in the presence of my father. As he had endeavored to train me in the way I should go, I knew the way; but the checkered scenes of my seafaring life had thrown me from the track, which I was trying now to regain."

Captain Bates reached his Massachusetts home in February, 1824, and remained with his family and friends several months. During this time a new brig named the Empress, of New Bedford, was launched, rigged, and fitted to his liking, and in August he sailed for Rio Janiero, touching at Richmond, Va., to finish the ship loading. On this passage his experience deepened, and he still advanced in reform. He says: —

"From the time I resolved to drink no more wine (in 1822), I had occasionally drank beer and cider. But now,

on weighing anchor from Hampton Roads, I decided from
henceforth to drink no ale, porter, beer, or cider, of any
description. My prospect for making a profitable and successful voyage was more flattering than my last; for I now
owned a part of the Empress and her cargo, and had the
confidence of my partners to sell and purchase cargoes as
often as it would prove to our advantage, and use my judgment about going to what part of the world I pleased. But
with all these many advantages to get rich, I felt sad and
homesick. I had provided myself with a number of what I
called interesting books, to read in my leisure hours. My
wife thought there were more novels and romances than
were necessary. In packing my trunk of books, she placed
a pocket New Testament, unknown to me, on the top of
them. On opening this trunk, I took up the New Testament, and found in the opening pages the following poem
by Mrs. Hemans, placed there to arrest my attention: —

> " 'Leaves have their time to fall,
>   And flowers to wither at the north wind's breath,
>   And stars to set — but all,
>   Thou hast *all* seasons for thine own, O Death!
>
> " 'Day is for mortal care,
>   Eve, for glad meetings round the joyous hearth,
>   Night, for the dreams of sleep, the voice of prayer,
>   But all for thee, thou mightiest of the earth.
>
> " 'Youth and the opening rose
>   May look like things too glorious for decay,
>   And smile at thee; but thou art not of those
>   That wait the ripened bloom to seize their prey.
>
> " 'We know when moons shall wane,
>   When summer birds from far shall cross the sea,
>   When autumn's hue shall tinge the golden grain,
>   But who shall teach us when to look for thee?
>
> " 'Is it when spring's first gale
>   Comes forth to whisper where the violets lie?
>   Is it when roses in our path grow pale?
>   They have one season — *all* are ours to die!
>
> " 'Thou art where billows foam;
>   Thou art where music melts upon the air;
>   Thou art around us in our peaceful home;
>   And the world calls us forth — and thou art there.'

"These lines did arrest my attention. I read them again and again. My interest in novels and romances ceased from that hour. Among the many books, I selected Doddridge's 'Rise and Progress of Religion in the Soul.' This and the Bible now interested me more than all other books."

The Empress arrived at Pernambuco, Brazil, October 30, where her commander was assailed by his associates, as he had been in other places, for refusing to take wine at dinner, as the practice was very common in South America :—

"A large company of us were dining with the American consul, Mr. Bennet. His lady, at the head of the table, filled her glass, and said, 'Captain Bates, shall I have the pleasure of a glass of wine with you?' I responded, and filled my glass with water. Mrs. B. declined, unless I would fill my glass with wine. She was aware, from our previous acquaintance, that I did not drink wine, but she felt disposed to induce me to disregard my former resolutions. As our waiting position attracted the attention of the company, one of them said, 'Why, Mr. Bates, do you refuse to drink Mrs. Bennet's health in a glass of wine?' I replied that I did not drink wine on any occasion, and begged Mrs. B. to accept my offer. She readily condescended, and drank my health in a glass of wine, and I hers in a glass of water.

"The topic of conversation now turned on wine-drinking, and my course in relation to it. Some concluded that a glass of wine would not injure any one. True, but the person who drank one glass would be likely to drink another, and another, until there was no hope of reform. Said one, 'I wish I could do as Captain Bates does; I should be much better off.' Another supposed I was a reformed drunkard. Surely there was no harm in drinking moderately. I endeavored to convince them that the better way to do up the business was *not to use it at all.* On another occasion a captain said to me, 'You are like old Mr. ——, of Nantucket ; he would n't drink sweetened water !'"

We pass over the Christian experience of Captain Bates, introducing only those points that seem closely connected with his advancement in moral reforms. It is sufficient here to state that in the fulfillment of resolutions made while on ship-board, he erected the family altar on his return home, and took the baptismal vow. At this time he suggested the first temperance society organized in that community, of which he speaks thus : —

"The same day, while we were changing our clothes, I solicited Elder M., who baptized me, to assist me in raising a temperance society. As my mind was now free with respect to this last duty, I was forcibly impressed with the importance of uniting my energies with others, to check, if possible, the increasing ravages of intemperance. Since I had ceased to use intoxicating drinks, I was constrained to look upon it as one of the most important steps that I had ever taken. Hence I ardently desired the same blessing for those around me. Elder M. was the first person whom I asked to aid me in this enterprise; failing with him, I moved out alone, and presented my paper for signers. Elder G., the Congregational minister, his two deacons, and a few of the principal men of the place, readily subscribed their names, twelve or thirteen in number, and forthwith a meeting was called, and the 'Fairhaven Temperance Society' was organized.

"The majority of our little number had been sea-captains, and had seen much of the debasing influence exerted by ardent spirits among its users, abroad and at home. They seemed the more ready, therefore, to give their names and influence to check this monster vice. Elder G. exclaimed, 'Why, Captain Bates, this is just what I have been wanting to see!' The meeting was organized by choosing Captain Stephen Merihew president, and Mr. Charles Drew secretary. Pending the discussion in adopting the constitution, it was voted that we pledge ourselves to abstain from the use of ardent spirits as a beverage. Having no precedent before us, it was voted that rum, gin, brandy, and whisky were ardent spirits. Wine, beer, and

cider were so freely used as beverages that the majority of
our members were then unwilling to have them in the list.
Some doubts arose with the minority whether we should
be able to maintain the spirit of our constitution without
abstaining from all intoxicating beverages. One of our
members, who had always been noted for doing much for
his visiting friends, said, 'Mr. President, what shall I do
when my friends come to visit me from Boston?' 'Do as
I do, Captain S.,' said another; 'I have not offered my
friends any liquor to drink in my house these ten years.'
'Oh, you are mistaken,' said the president, 'it is twenty!'
This doubtless was said because the man had ceased to
follow the fashion of treating his friends with liquor before
others were ready to join him.

"Inquiry was then made whether there were any temperance societies then known. A statement was made that
certain individuals in Boston had recently agreed together
that instead of purchasing their liquor in small quantities
at the stores, they would get it by the keg, and drink it
in their own houses. This association was called the 'Keg
Society.' If any temperance societies had ever been organized previous to the one at Fairhaven, we were unac-
quainted with the fact. A short time after our organization,
one of our number was reported to have violated his pledge.
This he denied. 'But you were intoxicated,' said we.
He declared that he had not drank anything but cider,
and that was allowed. We were told that his wife said
she would a great deal rather he would drink brandy; for
when he got drunk on cider he was much worse tempered.
During the trial of this member, he continued to declare
that he had not violated the letter of the constitution.
But it was evident to the society that he had violated
the intent and spirit of it, which he was unwilling to
admit, nor would he even promise to reform. He was
therefore expelled.

"The society now saw the necessity of amending the
constitution by striking out the words 'ardent spirits,' and
inserting in their place, 'all intoxicating drinks,' or some-

thing else that would sustain and aid the cause. From this a reform was introduced, which finally resulted in the disuse of all intoxicating drinks, except for medicinal purposes. This reform gave us the name of 'Teetotalers.'

"Before this, our temperance society had become exceedingly popular. Our meeting-houses, in their turn, were crowded with all classes to hear lectures on the subject; and converts, both male and female, by scores cheerfully pledged themselves to the temperance constitution. Many of the citizens of New Bedford who came to hear, also united with us. From thence a society was organized in their town, and in other places also. Arrangements were soon made, and a Bristol County Temperance Society was organized. The Massachusetts State Temperance Society soon followed. Temperance papers, tracts, and lecturers multiplied throughout the land, and opposition began to rage like the rolling sea, causing the tide of temperance to ebb awhile. Then came the 'Cold-Water Army,' of little children from four years upward, commingling their simple little songs in praise of water, pure cold water—no beverage like unmingled cold water. Their simple, stirring appeals, especially when assembled in their society meetings, seemed to give a new impetus to the cause, and re-arouse their parents to the importance of total abstinence from all intoxicating drinks. As I examined my papers the other day, I saw the book containing the names of nearly *three hundred children* who had belonged to our Cold-Water Army at Fairhaven."

Captain Bates retired from the seas in the month of June, 1828, having acquired more than a competency. He immediately began to devote his time and means to moral reforms, and labored ardently and successfully in this way for about twelve years, when he became an Adventist. He soon entered the lecture field, laboring both as a speaker and writer. In the cause of what he regarded as Bible truth and reform he employed his means and energies during the remainder of his useful life, a period of thirty-two years.

During his long ministry, reaching from the noon of life to old age, he lost none of his ardor in the cause of moral reform. In fact, his belief that the Son of God would soon come, with all the holy angels, to receive his people and take them to a pure heaven, gave double force to the inspired exhortations to purity of life, and the warnings to be ready for the coming of that day. While addressing the people upon the subject of being in readiness to meet the Lord at his coming, we have often heard him apply these texts with great force : " Take heed to yourselves, lest at any time your hearts be overcharged with surfeiting, and drunkenness, and cares of this life, and so that day come upon you unawares." " What agreement hath the temple of God with idols ? for ye are the temple of the living God ; as God hath said, I will dwell in them, and walk in them ; and I will be their God, and they shall be my people. Wherefore come out from among them, and be ye separate, saith the Lord, and touch not the unclean, and I will receive you, and will be a Father unto you, and ye shall be my sons and daughters, saith the Lord Almighty. Having therefore these promises, dearly beloved, let us cleanse ourselves from all filthiness of the flesh and spirit, perfecting holiness in the fear of God." " Know ye not that ye are the temple of God, and that the Spirit of God dwelleth in you ? If any man defile the temple of God, him shall God destroy ; for the temple of God is holy, which temple ye are." * When we expect a visit from friends whom we love and honor, how natural to put things in good order, and dress suitably for the occasion! This may well illustrate the action of those Adventists who are really such, in adopting the rules of clean, pure, practical hygiene.

Captain Bates began his table reform about the time he left his sea-faring life. He says : —

" From the year 1824, when I made my covenant with God, I had lived up to the principles of total abstinence from all intoxicating drinks, but had continued the use of tea and coffee, without much conviction as to their poi-

* Luke 21 : 34 ; 2 Cor. 6 : 16-18 ; 7 : 1 ; 1 Cor. 3 : 16, 17.

sonous and stimulating effects, for seven years longer. With my small stock of knowledge on the subject, I was unwilling to believe that these stimulants had any effect on me, until on a social visit with my wife at one of our neighbors', where tea was served us somewhat stronger than it was our usual habit to drink. It had such an effect on my whole system that I could not rest or sleep until after midnight. I then became fully satisfied — and have never since seen cause to change my belief — that it was the tea I had drank which so affected me. From thence I became convicted of its injurious qualities, and discarded the use of it.

"Soon after this, on the same principle, I ceased the use of coffee, so that it is now about thirty years since I have allowed myself knowingly to taste of either. If the reader should ask how much I have gained in this matter, I answer that my health is better, my mind is clearer, and my conscience in this respect is void of offense."

The writer first met Elder Bates at his home at Fairhaven, Mass., in the year 1846. He had at that time banished flesh-meats of all kinds, grease, butter, and spices, from his own plate. When asked why he did not use these things, his usual reply was, "I have eaten my share of them." He did not mention his views of proper diet in public at that time, nor in private, unless questioned upon the subject.

When I first became acquainted with Elder Bates, he was fifty-four years of age. His countenance was fair, his eye was clear and mild, his figure was erect and of fine proportions, and he was the last man to be picked out of the crowd as one who had endured the hardships and exposure of sea life, and who had come in contact with the demoralizing influences of such a life for more than a score of years. It had been eighteen years since he left the seas, and during that time his life of rigid temperance in eating, as well as in drinking, and his labors in the pure sphere of moral reform, had regenerated the entire man, body, soul, and spirit, until he seemed almost recreated for the special work to which God had called him. "Be ye clean that bear the vessels of the Lord." *

Elder Bates was a true gentleman. A man of great natural firmness and independence, after twenty-one years of sea-faring life, a large part of the time as commander of rough sailors — it might be supposed that he would be exacting and overbearing in his efforts to reform others. True, he would speak what he regarded as truth with great freedom and boldness; but after he had set forth principles, and urged the importance of obedience to them, he was willing to leave his hearers free to decide for themselves.

When many of his fellow-laborers embraced the principles of health reform, and began to advocate them (about the year 1860), he joined them in this work with great gladness of heart that he had sympathizers and fellow-workers in the cause. He now began to speak freely upon the subject, both in public and private. Up to this time he had refused all fruits and nuts because of the custom of eating them between meals. But when many of his brethren adopted only two meals a day, and furnished their tables with fruits and nuts, he would partake freely of them with his meals.

At a health reform convention held at Battle Creek, Mich., in the spring of 1871, Elder Bates, in his seventy-ninth year, made a speech of remarkable interest, into which he incorporated some items of his personal history and experience. He closed with the following summary of the benefits he had derived from adopting the principles of hygienic reform : —

"1. From the ruinous habits of a common sailor, by the help of the Lord I walked out into the ranks of sober, industrious, discerning men, who were pleased to employ and promote me in my calling, so that in the space of nine years I was supercargo and joint owner in the vessel and cargo which I commanded, with unrestricted commission to go where I thought best, and continue my voyage as long as I should judge best, for our interest.

* Isa. 52 : 11.

"The morning after my arrival in New York, among the laborers who came on board to discharge my vessel, was a Mr. Davis, one of my most intimate friends during my imprisonment. * We had spent many hours together talking over our dismal position, and the dreadful state and ruinous habits of our fellow-prisoners, and there agreed that if ever we were liberated, we would labor to avoid the dreadful habit of intemperance, and seek for a standing among sober, reflecting men. Now, aside from his associates, we conversed freely, and he readily admitted our feelings and resolutions in the past, but with sadness of heart acknowledged his lack of moral courage to reform ; and now, in this uncertain way, he was seeking for daily labor, when his poor state of health would admit of it.

"2. When I reached this point of total abstinence, God in mercy arrested my attention, and on the free confession of my sins, he, for his dear Son's sake, granted me his rich grace and pardoning mercy.

"3. Contrary to my former convictions, that if I was ever permitted to live to my present age I should be a suffering cripple, from my early exposure in following the sea, thanks be to God and our dear Lord and Saviour, whose rich blessing ever follows every personal effort to reform, that I am entirely free from aches and pains, with the gladdening, cheering prospect that if I continue to reform, and forsake every wrong, I shall, with the redeemed followers of the Lamb, stand 'without fault before the throne of God.'"

No comment on the foregoing is needed. And it is hardly necessary to state that this speech, from one who had reached nearly fourscore years, and who could look back upon a long life of self-control, marked all the way with new victories and new joys, electrified the audience. He then stood as straight as a monument, and could tread the side-walks as lightly as a fox. He stated that his

---

* Joseph Bates was impressed into British service in 1810. In 1812, refusing to fight against his country, he became a prisoner of war. He was released April 27, 1815, just five years from the time he was impressed.

digestion was perfect, and that he never ate and slept better at any period of his life.

Elder Bates held a large place in the hearts of his people. Those who knew him longest and best, esteemed him most highly. When his younger and most intimate fellow-laborers told him that his age should excuse him from the fatigue of itinerant life and public speaking, he laid off his armor as a captured officer would surrender his sword on the field of battle. The decision once made, he was as triumphant in faith and hope as before. Mrs. White wrote to him, recommending a nutritious diet, which called out the following characteristic statements from his pen, written in February, 1872, about forty days before his death : —

"God bless you, Sister White, for your favor of yesterday, the 13th. You say I must have good, nutritious food. I learn from report that I am starving myself, and am withholding from my daughter, who is with me, and alone a good part of the time in my absence ; and that when I ask a blessing at my table, I ask the Lord to bless that which I may eat, and not that which is on the table. This is what I am not guilty of, nor ever was in all my family worship for some fifty years, but *once ;* and I do greatly marvel how my industrious neighbors found out this one exception. But I will tell you the circumstance.

"Several years ago I was with the church in Vassar, Tuscola Co., Mich., and was invited to address them and their children in a barn on the Fourth of July, and also to take dinner with them. The tables were soon up, and loaded with tempting eatables ; and I was invited to ask the blessing. The swine's flesh upon the table I knew was abominable and unclean, and that God had positively, by law, forbidden the eating or touching of it. See Lev. 11 : 7, 8 (*law,* verse 46) ; also Deut. 14 : 1–3, 8. I therefore very quietly distinguished, and asked a blessing on the clean, nutritious, wholesome, *lawful* food. Some whispered, and some smiled, others looked, and so on.

"Starving, with more than enough to eat! Now allow me to state what, by the providence and blessing of God, we have in our house from which to choose a daily bill of fare: —

"GRAINS.

"90 pounds of superfine white flour.
"100 pounds of graham flour.
"5 bushels of choice garden corn.
"Pop and sweet corn in abundance.
"Cornmeal, rice, and oatmeal.
"Cornstarch, butter, sugar, salt.

"VEGETABLES.

"Three varieties of potatoes.
"Sweet turnips, parsnips, squashes.
"Two varieties of onions.

"FRUITS.

"11 cans of preserved sweet peaches.
"6 cans of sweet grapes.
"Strawberries preserved and dried.
"Quince and grape jelly.
"Tomatoes by the jug.
"20 pounds of dried sweet peaches.
"Box of Isabella grapes, almost consumed.
"Three varieties of apples and quinces.

"But the people say, and think they know what they say, that he refuses to furnish his table with tea and coffee. That's true! They are poison. Some thirty-five years ago I was using both tea and coffee. After retiring from a tea-party at midnight, my companion said, 'What is the matter? Can't you lie quiet and sleep?' 'Sleep! no,' I said. 'Why not?' was the next question. 'Oh! I wish Mrs. Bunker's tea had been in the East Indies. It's poison.' Here I forever bade adieu to tea and coffee. After awhile my wife joined me, and we banished them from our table and dwelling. That's the reason they are not on my table.

"They say, too, that this man does not allow any ardent spirits or strong drink in his house. That's true. Please hear my reason: Fifty years ago I was by myself on the boundless ocean. My thoughts troubled me. Said

I to Him who always hears, 'I'll never drink another glass of grog or strong drink while I live.' That's why I have no intoxicating drink on or about my premises.

"Well, there is another thing that he is fanatical about, and differs from more than half his country-men. What is that?—He will not have about him nor use any tobacco. Guilty! My reason: Forty-eight years ago I was away toward the setting sun; our gallant ship was plowing her way through the great Pacific. During the nightwatch we were called to take some refreshment. I then tossed my chew of tobacco into the ocean, never, no, never, to touch, taste, or handle any more. And allow me to say that when I had gained the victory over this deadening, besotting, benumbing vice, I went on deck the next morning a better man than ever I was in all my former life. Why?—I was free. I could appreciate God's handiwork in sea and sky, even in the tumbling, rolling waves. I could breathe freely, inhaling the pure air of heaven, and shout. I was a free man.

"Therefore, if any demand is ever made on me for tobacco, tea, coffee, or strong drink of any kind that intoxicates, they must present an order from the Court above.

"Here comes half a barrel of graham crackers, and a lot of farina, a national breadstuff of the native South Americans. I think I am now well supplied with good, nutritious food. And if there is any lack, I have some good, faithful brethren who seem to be waiting to serve me.

"I am your brother, now on retired pay in Monterey, Mich. "JOSEPH BATES.

"*Feb. 14, 1872.*"

Elder Joseph Bates died at Battle Creek, Mich., March 19, 1872, in the eightieth year of his age. His last hours, though characterized by pain such as few men have been called upon to pass through, afforded marked evidence of the superiority of faith in Christ over bodily suffering and the prospect of certain and rapidly approaching death.

Having in early manhood chosen the service of God, and having for many years faithfully endeavored to live the life of the righteous, his last end was such as those alone can expect who have sedulously endeavored to preserve a conscience void of offense toward God and man.

As we close this sketch, we are impressed with the words of Paul, prompted by a review of his own past life, and the reward of the glorious future: "I have fought a good fight, I have finished my course, I have kept the faith. Henceforth there is laid up for me a crown of righteousness, which the Lord, the righteous Judge, shall give me at that day; and not to me only, but unto all them also that love his appearing."

ELDER J. N. ANDREWS.

John Nevins Andrews was born at Poland, Maine, July 22, 1829. His paternal ancestors were among the early colonists of this country, having landed at Plymouth eighteen years after the arrival of the Mayflower, and settled at Taunton, Mass. In the Indian wars that followed, nearly the entire family were massacred. As the male members of the family, with the exception of one sick boy, who remained at home, were at work in a field, the Indians surprised them, and got between them and their guns. They were men of high stature, and of great physical strength; and in their determination to sell their lives as dearly as possible, they tore up trees of considerable size, and used them as weapons. But the contest was unequal, and the well-armed Indians killed them all.

"Both my grandfathers," says Elder Andrews, in a sketch from his own pen, "served in the Revolutionary War. Their names were David Andrews and John Nevins. The name of the latter was given to me. Grandfather Nevins was a man remarkable for his piety and kindness of heart. He lived to be very aged.

"My earliest religious conviction was at the age of five years, when I heard a discourse by Daniel B. Randall from these words: 'And I saw a great white throne, and Him that sat on it, from whose face the earth and the heaven fled away.' So vivid was the impression made upon my mind that I have rarely read the passage without remembering that discourse. But it was not until I was thirteen years old that I found the Saviour. This was in January, 1843. I then became deeply interested in the doctrine of Christ's near coming, and I have ever since cherished this faith."

Elder Andrews entered upon the work of the Christian ministry in 1850, at the age of twenty-one, and for twenty-seven years has been a close fellow-laborer and an intimate friend of the writer. He is tall, with slender chest and massive brain. When he entered the ministry, he was afflicted with sore throat and a cough, and it was the general opinion among his friends that consumption would terminate his life in a few years. His thirst for education was great, yet he could spare neither the time nor the means to take a regular course in school.

His labors as a preacher and writer have been excessive, and he has taxed his strength severely by continuous study. Yet his health has been improving since 1864, when his attention was called to the subject of health reform. As we have before stated, his prospects for life and health, when he entered the ministry in 1850, were most gloomy. And that he should recover health while laboring intensely hard, depriving himself of seasons of recreation, and frequently cutting short the proper periods of sleep, furnishes the strongest proof of the benefits of hygienic reform.

In 1871 a personal friend requested him to write his experience for another friend in Providence, R. I. Of this request Elder Andrews says: —

"In asking me to write directly to his friend, my correspondent truthfully remarks that 'many people will not believe what appears in papers or periodicals, but a

personal account will always suffice to remove old prejudices.' Now there is a reason for this unbelief and dis-
trust that is certainly very weighty. The press teems
with accounts of wonderful cures wrought by such and
such medicines ; and the point of each statement is this :
'If you would have health, buy this marvelous remedy.'
Sensible people long ago decided that these certificates
were in the great majority of cases entirely unreliable,
and that they were formed for the manifest purpose of
enriching the proprietor of 'the matchless sanative' that
they respectively extol.

"Now, why should not health reformers be as generally
and as promptly discredited as should the venders of the
various 'magic cordials' and 'healing balsams' everywhere
offered 'for the relief of suffering humanity'? They should,
if they can be justly classed together. And if the same
principle governs the action of each, then let them share
in the same condemnation.

"But observe the contrast : The advocates of the hygienic system declare, as a fundamental principle, that
health can be regained or preserved only upon condition
that we 'cease to do evil and learn to do well ;' while
the dealers in the aforesaid wonderful preparations sev-
erally state, as one of the most convincing reasons for
the use of their respective medicines, that 'no change of
diet or of habits of life is required in order to be benefited by this wonderful remedy.'

"The first party declares that the restorative power
exists only in the vital forces which God has given us ;
the other, that it is to be found in drugs. The one affirms
that the restorative power within ourselves can alone give
us health, but will do it only upon condition of abstinence
from wrong habits, and of simple obedience to the laws of
our being. But the other replies in derision, 'This is all
humbug ; you may eat, drink, and act as you will, without any danger of evil consequences, provided you freely
use my healing balm.'

"Which of these parties is entitled to our confidence?

One of them asks no money, but insists that we govern ourselves by the laws which the Author of our being has established within our own organization. The other bids us freely disobey, and promises us immunity from evil consequences on condition that we use the medicines which they desire us to buy at their hands.

"We know which of these two kinds of teaching is the more enticing to the multitudes; but would it not be well to ask which is the more reasonable? One of them declares that obedience to the laws of life is the one condition upon which we can have health. The other asserts that God has provided means whereby men may deliberately disobey those laws, and yet escape the consequences of that disobedience; and that that means is something known only to the ones who say this, and to be had only on condition that you pay them well for it. On which side are reason and common sense? on that of self-control, or on that of self-indulgence? And which of these two classes is attempting to get your money upon false pretenses?

"I am a firm believer in the principles of health reform. I have cause to be such. My judgment is convinced that its principles are reasonable, and just, and true. Moreover, I have proved them true by the test of actual experience. In this thing, therefore, I speak not merely that which I have heard, but I also testify that which I know. I believed in the health reform when I first learned its principles, because to me they were self-evident truths. But there is no teacher like experience. Ever after I was first instructed in this system, I believed it to be true; but the experience of seven years enables me to speak now as one who knows whereof he affirms.

"I do not attempt to instruct the people in physiological and hygienic science. There are plenty to do this who are fully competent to the task. I speak rather as members of the church bear testimony after the sermon of their pastor, not to give instruction in the doctrines set forth, but to declare that I have proved these very things to be true, and to testify that I know the certainty of that wherein we have been instructed.

"And why should I not speak with much assurance? I know what were the difficulties under which I labored eight years ago, and I well understand that my present condition is in marked contrast to my state at that time. Then I was a feeble man from head to foot. Now I have found entire relief from all the difficulties under which I suffered, and in God's merciful providence have excellent health.

"I can hardly recall any period of my early life in which I was a possessor of firm health. In boyhood, my growth was rapid, but I never saw the time when my physical strength was fully equal to that of most of those of my years. I loved severe study much more ardently than I did any of the sports and pastimes of my associates. From my earliest childhood I was taught to shun evil associates, and was warned against intemperance in every form in which my parents understood it to exist; but I was not instructed in the principles of hygiene, for neither my father nor my mother had any just knowledge of these.

"I was kept from the use of tobacco, and from even tasting strong drink; but I learned almost nothing of the evils of unwholesome food — at least, of such as was common in our own family. I did not know that late suppers, and 'hearty' ones at that, were serious evils. I had no idea of any special transgression in eating between meals; and though this was mostly confined to fruit, I did herein ignorantly transgress to a very considerable extent. I supposed old cheese was good to aid digestion! Do not smile at my folly; unless my memory is at fault, I had learned this out of 'standard medical works.' As to mince-pie and sausage, I had no thought that these were unwholesome, unless too highly seasoned, or, as it was termed, 'made too *rich*.' Hot biscuit and butter, doughnuts, pork in every form, pickles, preserves, tea, coffee, etc., etc., were all in common use. Of ventilation I understood almost nothing. And I might continue to enumerate the particulars of my ignorance of vital hygienic truth, but it would be easier to tell what I knew than to attempt to mention that which I ought to have known but did not.

"But I must also expose my ignorance, by confessing that I had little other idea of headache, dyspepsia, nausea, fevers, etc., than that these were, for the most part, wholly beyond our control, and that, like the various phenomena of nature, they were ordered by God's hand, and man had generally no agency therein. Do not smile at this strange notion. It is strange, indeed, that such ideas should prevail; but that they do prevail, even now, you may satisfy yourself by calling out the ideas of the very next person you meet.

"When I entered the Christian ministry, at the age of twenty-one, I did not enjoy firm health. Though in no sense an intemperate man, as the word is commonly used, I did, nevertheless, have no just idea of Christian temperance. However much I lacked in other respects, I did not lack in zeal to labor in the work I had undertaken; and I think I may say in truth that I felt in some degree the responsibility of my calling. My anxiety of mind was constant, and oftentimes extreme. Associated with a few others in the defense, or rather in the attempt to advance, an unpopular truth, there fell to my lot a heavy burden of anxious care, and the necessity of much overtaxing labor, oftentimes requiring not the day merely, but much, or even all, of the night.

"But one cannot violate the laws of his being, even in the best of causes, without suffering the consequences; and so I found, to my own cost. Had I understood the laws of life in the right use of food, and in the principles of hygiene generally, I could have gone longer than I did in the exhausting labor which I attempted to sustain. But, in short, my story is this: In less than five years I was utterly prostrated. My voice was destroyed, I supposed permanently; my eyesight was considerably injured; I could not rest by day, and I could not sleep well at night;

I was a serious sufferer from dyspepsia; and as to that mental depression which attends this disease, I think I have a sufficient acquaintance with it to dispense with it in time to come, if right habits of life will enable one to do so. On arising in the morning it was very generally the case that the sensation in my stomach was as though a living creature were devouring it. Often, without apparent reason, very great prostration would come over me. My brain, from severe taxation and from ignorance on my part of the proper manner of performing brain labor, had become much diseased, and seemed to be undergoing the process called 'softening.' It was only at times that I could perform mental labor to any extent. I was considerably troubled with salt-rheum, which made the middle finger of each hand raw on both sides much of the time. I had plenty of headache, though I thought little of that. But I had one difficulty which made life a heavy burden to me. I had catarrh to such an extent that my head seemed to be incurably diseased. I will not describe its disagreeable peculiarities, but will simply say that I have not often seen persons who have it in so very bad a form as mine. No other ill of life ever gave me such trouble as this. My general strength was prostrated; I was a burden to myself, and could not but be such to others.

"Some nine years of my life elapsed after my general prostration, before I learned anything of consequence respecting the subject of health reform. During this time, from laying aside mental labor to a large extent, and working in the open air, I had received considerable benefit so far as my general strength was concerned. But I need not further state my own troubles in the past. Thank God that I can say 'in the *past*.' For the opportunity to say this, I am indebted to the health reform."

In the *Health Reformer* for 1872, Elder Andrews related his own experience and that of his family in adopting health reform. From his narrative we quote:—

"My attention was especially called to this subject in the early part of 1864. At that time my son Charles, who was then six years of age, was in a very critical condition. His left leg was withered its entire length, and was much smaller than his right one. Fortunately, however, it was not shorter than the other. His left ankle was greatly enlarged from a scrofulous deposit, which was almost as hard as bone. The ankle joint was therefore almost entirely stiff. In hobbling along, for he could not be said to walk, he turned his foot as far round as the foot can be turned, so that the toe was something more than at a right angle with the other foot, and actually pointed back. His general health was much impaired. He complained much at night of pain in his back. His difficulties began when he was about two years of age, and gradually reached the state which I have described. My wife and I were deeply distressed. We often prayed God to teach us what to do. We had our son examined by physicians and surgeons, but they were quite at a loss what to say to us."

It was finally decided to place the child where he could receive hygienic treatment. Elder Andrews continues : —

"Fifteen weeks of strict hygienic living and of judicious water treatment wrought in my son a change little short of miraculous. He walked in a natural manner, the enlargement of the ankle joint had nearly disappeared, and the withered leg had begun to grow. He continued to gain in health and strength, for his mode of life at home was the same as that under which such great changes had been wrought. His health became firm, and his left leg became equal in size and strength to the right. He has possessed vigorous health to the present time. When we placed him under hygienic treatment, his mother and myself determined to fully adopt the principles of health reform, and this we did in serious earnest, not with any particular expectation of benefit to ourselves, but because it seemed plainly right. I certainly had no idea of any manifest personal advantage in the recovery of my own health.

"We adopted the two-meal system, and have strictly adhered to it till the present time. We put away from our table, spice, pepper, vinegar, etc. We also put away butter, meat, and fish, and substituted graham for fine flour. But we endeavored to secure plenty of good fruit, and, with our vegetables and grains, we have always used some milk and a very little salt. We have strictly abstained from eating anything except in connection with our meals, and have taught our children to act on this plan. For a space of time we took a brief season for rest each day, before the second meal. This plan of rest-hour, however, we have not regularly followed for several years past, but have occasionally regarded it, as necessity has demanded. But we have tried faithfully to follow the hygienic system in every essential point. And now to state its consequences in my own case : —

" 1. One of the first results which I observed upon the change made in my diet, was that my food had once more the keen relish which I can remember it possessed in my childhood, but which it had long since lost.

" 2. Headache, dizziness, nausea, and the like, were gone.

" 3. But several months elapsed before I found any increase of strength. Nor is this strange when I state that, though I made so great a change in my living, and withal omitted the third meal, I did, nevertheless, continue my labors as before the change. But after some months I became sensible of an increase of strength, and this continued to be the case till I could say in strict truth that I possessed greater strength and power of endurance than at any former period of my life.

" 4. One of the immediate consequences of omitting my third meal was entire freedom from morning faintness. When I dispensed with suppers, I also closed my acquaintance with what seemed to be a living creature gnawing in my stomach each morning before breakfast. I thus found that it was not the lack of food of which my stomach complained, but quite the reverse. It had toiled all night to dispose of the supper, when it should have had rest.

"5. And as to the strength derived from a hygienic diet, I have this testimony to bear, that whereas I often suffered from faintness under the common method of living, I have no recollection of one case of this kind in my own experience for the whole period of my present course of life. I have often remarked that I can omit one of my two meals with less inconvenience than formerly I could one of the three.

"6. As the direct consequence of omitting unhygienic articles from my diet, my salt-rheum has wholly disappeared. Boils used to be frequent with me, but I have not had one in eight years. And the painful sores which came upon my under lip every few weeks in former years, have absolutely discontinued their visitations. These things I attribute largely to the entire disuse of butter.

"7. When I adopted the health reform, I had, as I supposed, an incurable catarrh. I was ignorant of the fact that it was caused by an inability of the liver to keep up with its work while its owner was continually taking into the stomach substances which would vastly increase its work beyond the design of the Creator. But after some months of correct living, especially in the matter of diet, I found some intervals of relief from the terrible scourge. Then it seemed as bad as ever. Then after a time there came a longer period of relief. Then again a relapse, and then a still longer season of freedom. So it continued for nearly two years, when to my great joy it ceased to come back at all.

"I owe to God a debt of gratitude for the health reform, which I can never repay or even fully express. It is to me something sacred, constituting, as Christian temperance, an essential part of true religion. In one respect only do I knowingly allow myself to transgress, and that is in the endeavor to discharge the responsibilities which devolve upon me, which sometimes requires a large part of the twenty-four hours. Yet with the strength derived from correct living in other respects, I hope not to destroy myself by thus laboring at times beyond what I would approve in secular business."

[Some years after the paragraphs above quoted were written, Elder Andrews went to Switzerland, where he labored most arduously for many years in the establishment of the Central European Mission, located at Basle. While he lived, almost the entire burden of this important work rested upon his shoulders; and under the pressure of great responsibility, cares, and duties to which he had not been accustomed, and of the new and perplexing difficulties incident to pioneer work in a foreign field, the disposition to labor far beyond his strength, which for many years had led him to deprive himself of proper opportunity for sleep and recreation, was indulged even to a greater extent than in previous years. In addition to this extraordinary strain upon his physical powers, he was in a new country, where health principles were little known, and was surrounded with most unfavorable conditions as regards diet, ventilation, and the disposal of waste. For years the house in which he lived was thoroughly permeated with sewer-gas. Surrounded thus with conditions most inimical to health, it is not surprising that Elder Andrews finally succumbed to the pressure of untoward circumstances. Oct. 21, 1883, at the age of fifty-five years, he died of consumption, after battling for more than three years with the disease. He continued his labors almost to the very close of his life. Few men have left behind them a record of greater purity of life, or of more earnest effort for Christ and humanity. His indefatigable labors did more, perhaps, than those of any other man, to develop the Bible evidence of the views advocated by this people; and the debt of gratitude which we owe him should lead us to study earnestly the principles that he loved so well, and to emulate his noble example in a life of temperance and self-sacrifice, and of devotion to the good of others.]

We'd love to have you download our catalog of
titles we publish at:

www.TEACHServices.com

or write or email us your thoughts,
reactions, or criticism about this
or any other book we publish at:

TEACH Services, Inc.
254 Donovan Road
Brushton, NY 12916

info@TEACHServices.com

or you may call us at:

518/358-3494